TESTIMONIALS

"Filled with hopeful messages, gut wrenching truths, and a brave and resilient spirit, Karla's journey into the darkness and back again is captivating and life changing."

—**Annie Grace**
Author of *This Naked Mind*

"If you're questioning your relationship with alcohol, read this book. *And She Came Tumbling Down* has everything: raw storytelling, honesty, vulnerability, aha moments, and redemption. Karla challenges the status quo around acceptable drinking in our boozy culture."

—**Michelle Smith**
Certified Alcohol and Drug Counselor and Founder of Recovery is the New Black

"Few people are strong enough to be as candid about the most vulnerable parts of their story as Karla Adkins is. The world is a much better place thanks to her honesty and compassion and the unforgettable truths she shares. *And She Came Tumbling Down* will save people's lives."

—**Marah Stets**
New York Times Bestselling Writer, Editor

"Hearing an authentic, compassionate voice from someone who has blazed an alcohol-free trail for others to follow has given me the courage to follow that same trail step by step. For those of us who have been trapped by the addiction of alcohol (and there are so many of us), it can feel like a lonely, hopeless place. But Karla's story and especially her successful escape from the assassin's hands gives all of us hope while assuring us that we are indeed not alone. Karla paints a crystal-clear picture of how alcohol became a false friend that nearly annihilated her liver and thereby almost killed her. But it's her transformation out of the depths of despair that is really going to help people like me to see that there is another way of living … and living extremely well … without the toxic poison of alcohol. And for those who joke about alcohol and its effect on one's health (and again … there are so many of us … I know this, as I used to be one of them), I hope this book serves as a much-needed wake-up call."

—**Chad David Smith**
Client and Software Executive

"Karla's story is not only relatable and timely, it's one that has a message we all need to hear. Karla has taken her experiences and created a space to help others in a clinically appropriate and professional way, leaving the person feeling fully seen and heard. As a professional counselor and trauma therapist, I fully believe that her skill set, competency, and understanding of the whole person will bring radical change to the field of addiction. Her message brings hope to many and has helped me change the way I see alcohol and its impact on the whole person. Karla writes with the same passion and zest for life as how she truly lives."

—**Jody G. Dumphy, LPC**

AND SHE CAME TUMBLING DOWN

AND SHE CAME TUMBLING DOWN

Breaking the Bonds of Alcohol and Creating a Life of Freedom

KARLA ADKINS

PYP Publish Your Purpose

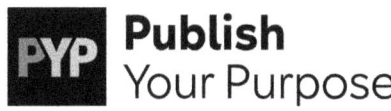

Copyright © 2022 Karla Adkins. All rights reserved.

No part of this publication shall be reproduced, transmitted, or sold in whole or in part in any form without prior written consent of the author, except as provided by the United States of America copyright law. Any unauthorized usage of the text without express written permission of the publisher is a violation of the author's copyright and is illegal and punishable by law. All trademarks and registered trademarks appearing in this guide are the property of their respective owners.

For permission requests, write to the publisher, addressed "Attention: Permissions Coordinator," at the address below.

Publish Your Purpose
141 Weston Street, #155
Hartford, CT, 06141

The opinions expressed by the Author are not necessarily those held by Publish Your Purpose.

Ordering Information: Quantity sales and special discounts are available on quantity purchases by corporations, associations, and others. For details, contact the publisher at orders@publishyourpurposepress.com.

Edited by: Nancy Graham-Tillman, Chloë Siennah
Cover photography by: Allison Duff of Alli D. Photography
Illustrations by: Chrissie Bonner of Illustrating Progress
Cover design by: Cornelia Murariu
Typeset by: Medlar Publishing Solutions Pvt Ltd., India

Printed in the United States of America.
ISBN: 978-1-955985-65-9 (hardcover)
ISBN: 978-1-955985-64-2 (paperback)
ISBN: 978-1-955985-66-6 (ebook)

Library of Congress Control Number: 2022910154

First edition, September 2022.

The information contained within this book is strictly for informational purposes. The material may include information, products, or services by third parties. As such, the Author and Publisher do not assume responsibility or liability for any third-party material or opinions. The publisher is not responsible for websites (or their content) that are not owned by the publisher. Readers are advised to do their own due diligence when it comes to making decisions.

Publish Your Purpose is a hybrid publisher of non-fiction books. Our authors are thought leaders, experts in their fields, and visionaries paving the way to social change—from food security to anti-racism. We give underrepresented voices power and a stage to share their stories, speak their truth, and impact their communities. Do you have a book idea you would like us to consider publishing? Please visit PublishYourPurpose.com for more information.

To my husband Grady,
Thank you for loving me when most would have
walked away. Without you this book would not
be possible
Piper Gray- Mama loves you more than all the leaves
On the trees and the water in the sea. I want better for
you in this world.

To all of you that I have worked with while
Writing this book, you know who you are.
Thank you for the safe space to share
my story, and getting vulnerable and sharing your own.
We can do hard things.
Let's do this.

CONTENTS

Foreword .... *xv*

Introduction .... *xxv*

Section 1
The Climb

Chapter 1: Anxiety Ridden 3

Chapter 2: The Best Laid Plans 9

Chapter 3: Pink Ice 13

Chapter 4: The Downward Spiral 21

Chapter 5: Yellow 27

Chapter 6: And then She Came Tumbling Down 33

Chapter 7: The Tilting of Heads and Blessing of Hearts 41

Chapter 8: Back to Darkness, My Old Friend.............................45

Section 2
Healing On My Own Terms

Chapter 9: Bubble Baths & Popsicle Sticks.................................53

Chapter 10: Dinners, Parties, and Book Clubs, Oh My...............57

Chapter 11: Why Me? 61

Chapter 12: Roots 65

Chapter 13: My Walk of Shame 73

Chapter 14: My Name is Karla and I'm Not an Alcoholic.........79

Chapter 15: Finding My People 85

Chapter 16: My Battle Wound 89

Section 3
Looking Through A New Lens

Chapter 17: Removing the Invisible Yoke 95

Chapter 18: Rearview Mirror Check..99

Chapter 19: And Now a Word From … Smokey Bear.............109

Chapter 20: Changing the Narrative 119

Conclusion 125

Afterword.. 129

About the Author 145

I left the hospital late last Friday night, with that same dark, lost, and hopeless feeling. I had just left the bedside of a patient with cirrhosis and acute alcohol-associated hepatitis. This young man, not yet 30, was preparing to die, his impending death loosely classified a "death of despair." His mom cried and his wife nodded slowly with tears lingering on the rims of her eyelids as she rocked their toddler. No one questioned further why he didn't qualify for a liver transplant or why going home with hospice was his only option. After four weeks of improved nutrition, steroids, and alcohol abstinence, I couldn't turn around his jaundice, confusion, infections, and bleeding. When I first met him, belly distended with ascites and eyes deeply yellow, I asked him if he could commit to abstinence. He told me he wasn't sure alcohol caused his problem. The next day, when I asked him the same question after telling him he had a 50 percent chance of surviving another month, he responded he was 80 percent sure he would never drink again. That vulnerable and truthful statement disqualified him for further consideration of a life-saving liver transplant. Despite facing the loss of his life and all that came with it, his brain was still negotiating the possibility of drinking again. To some, this seems like lunacy, but the brain will negotiate anything it wants when alcohol has taken hold at this stage. It is a state of total unawareness, akin to being under a spell or hypnotized. Very few can break free from the spell. For so many, it is simply too late and the consequence of being unaware is death.

How does one become aware and break free of alcohol and the downward spiral it causes? Prevention seems impossible when alcohol billboards line the thoroughfares leading to schools, happy hour is not "happy hour" without alcohol, and the simple act of naming a boat isn't official without breaking a bottle of champagne on the bow. Alcohol has embedded its barbs into the fiber of our culture. Self-soothing depression and anxiety with a legal, readily available, and relativity inexpensive bottle of liquor is seemingly easier than waiting months for an appointment and paying out of pocket for a mental health provider. While there are efforts to develop medications to block or reverse the negative effects of alcohol on the liver, they don't change the fact that people use alcohol for the effect it has on the brain. While drinking can start as an innocuous way to relax and socially lubricate, every human who drinks a single drop runs the risk of developing tolerance and physiologic dependence on alcohol. The brain eventually does not feel normal without alcohol and the dosage to get the original reward escalates to the point where organ toxicity happens. The liver slowly develops scar tissue, progressing to cirrhosis in the background. As alcohol use escalates, heavy binges are needed just to feel "normal." The brain can't get enough to drink but the liver can't take another drop. At this point, the liver can develop acute alcohol-associated hepatitis, a rapidly progressive form of liver failure, at which point most become too sick to drink. Sadly, some manage to drink through the nausea and vomiting just to try to feel less tremulous. Some drink to stave off alcohol withdrawal seizure, even though they literally hate drinking. This cycle of drinking in the face of feeling awful just to feel better is often done in private and carries with it deep guilt and shame. I met Karla at this stage of her life, when I was just a medical student. It was before her awakening and before I would begin my own journey into helping others approaching death from drinking.

The stigma Karla experienced in the hospital was real. The doctors would shake their heads and mutter "what a waste" as they left her room. I could imagine the pain she felt from their judgement back then, but reading her story now, I know the full extent of her turmoil. As medical professionals, we are skilled at getting patients vital signs within acceptable parameters for discharge. The first time Karla left the hospital, was she well? Was the illness in her mind addressed at all during the hospitalization? Sure, she was told, "you can never drink again" with an implied "or else." But how was she expected to do that? She couldn't. Towards the end of her first hospitalization, I'll never forget the moment that Karla opened up: "Maybe I am drinking more than I think I am. I'm going to have to do some self-reflection."

When Karla was readmitted, sick again after relapsing, the shame she carried was deadlier than her recurrent jaundice. After getting her back to "discharge criteria" with medical therapies, I feared she would still die. I had nothing to give her from a textbook that would help. Terrified, I sat beside her in a dark hospital room and took a risk that I now call therapeutic empathy. Brene Brown coined the phrase "empathy is the antidote to shame." I challenge all healthcare providers who have lost a loved one to alcohol or who know first-hand the turmoil of keeping a bottle on hand to soothe their own day to sit beside their patients in solidarity.

Sobriety has little to do with resources, intelligence, or fortitude. Sobriety is an awakening of the mind and a shift into reality that comes with courageously combating the deadliest effect of alcohol on the mind: shame. With Karla's soul-bearing testimony, the world has an empathetic partner for the battle.

—**Loretta Jophlin, M.D., Ph.D**

FOREWORD xix

Dear Reader,

I know how scary this is. I really do. You're just trying to "fix" this nightmare that you're living in. The world doesn't stop moving when you're slowly sinking. I feel you. I can almost feel your exhaustion and hear the "what ifs" that are taking over your thoughts. *What if someone finds out? What if they put it on my medical record? What if it impacts my insurance? What if they label me? What if they tell me I can never drink again?* All these thoughts and so many more are stressing you out. Right now your body is heavy, and the plates you've been spinning to try and make everything work are falling. And you have this one tool in your toolbox that you've used to help with stress, exhaustion, and feeling overwhelmed. Alcohol. The very thing that's taking you down. It's become a vicious cycle.

What if we changed the "what if" game a little bit and you started asking yourself different questions: *What if I can break free? What if I didn't have to do this anymore? What if I didn't even think about alcohol anymore? What if there were no labels? What if I became a healthy version of myself?*

That healthy version of you is in there waiting for someone to pull it out, and that someone is you. Your body is giving you signs that this substance just isn't serving you anymore. What will it take for you to listen?

I know you can't imagine a life without drinking alcohol. I get it. It seems like life would be so dark and always full of struggle. What if it wasn't? What if life was finally bright again? I have been where you are now. I want to offer you hope for a better future than the one you imagine now. When I was lying in a hospital bed, I was thinking that my life was over. I thought I'd never fit in or have fun and that I'd have to go to daily meetings just to get through each day. I wish someone had told me it didn't have to be that way. I'm so thankful for that glimmer of hope my physician gave me on that dark, gloomy day.

Your body is giving you signs. It's tired. It's so easy to put the blame on other things and other people, but what about the most powerful advocate you have? You! You're seeing physicians to try to fix everything—except one thing. Can you see the power alcohol is holding over you?

You never intended to get here. Nobody starts drinking with the intention of it seeping into all areas of their life. Since you were young, you've been groomed to love this substance. It's been painted in such a romantic, beautiful light since you can remember. You watched people drink. You watched it be a normal way of life, a normal way to celebrate, a normal way to grieve. You have been duped into believing that alcohol helps your problems when all along it's been the culprit. That's not your fault. But you *are* responsible for getting control back.

You aren't powerless. Actually, you're more powerful than you ever imagined. We feel so powerless because we're looking in the wrong place. We're constantly trying to put rules around our drinking, and when we fail, we're so angry at ourselves. When was the last time you got angry at the substance? We've trained our bodies to function with alcohol, so that also means we can train our bodies and brains to function without it.

Are you stuck in your story? I know I was years ago. I just couldn't seem to get out of the cycle of feeling bad for myself and my circumstances. I know this may come off as harsh, but we are in this together, so we should be able to have tough conversations. What will it take for you to stop the broken record of telling yourself you need alcohol, or that you'll stop drinking once life isn't so hard? I get it, some of you are going through difficult things like divorce, loss of a loved one, financial crisis, infidelity … I could keep this list going, but you get my point. When we use alcohol as a tool or a medication, we play a very dangerous game.

I met with a beautiful young woman once and my heart ached as soon as I saw her face. I saw my face in hers. The face of someone whose body was tired from being fed poison. I recognized her red hue and puffiness from my own journey. I was actually excited to help, and I knew I could because our journeys were so similar. She had been using "Dr. Google" and checking her rearview mirror for yellow eyes just like I had. Unfortunately, she just couldn't consider walking away from alcohol until her hard stuff was over. She would say, "Just let me get through this divorce and I will call, I promise." Well, she and I would never get the chance to meet again. Alcohol extinguished the light inside of her and it was over. A woman with so much more life to live was gone. I really was no different than her, but I think my spirit wasn't quite broken yet like hers was.

If I could go back to when I was struggling and tell myself something, I think it would be that freedom from alcohol is very real. I wouldn't have to spend my life always wanting to drink, and someday the taste of it would actually turn me off. Years ago, when my husband and I were at a fundraiser, he went to get a drink and asked me if I wanted anything. I asked for a Diet Coke. He came back with his drink and mine, which looked just alike. "Is this one mine?" I asked, to be sure. He assured me I had the right one, so I went in for a gulp. Grady drinks regular Coke so I figured if I got the wrong drink, all I would be getting was a big hit of that sugary taste. Except this time his drink was a bourbon and Coke, and I drank down a mouthful of it. I was livid. He felt horrible. We ended the night early, and I gave him the silent treatment all the way home. I tried to brush my teeth and suck on mints, but the nasty taste of liquor lingered in my mouth. But it wasn't just the taste that bothered me. I was scared that the alcohol monster would be woken up inside me. You see, that's what society tells you, that just the taste of alcohol will bring back the cravings, the pull. Because you are powerless, right? As I stewed over the events of the evening, clarity came. It just wasn't true. The gulp only gave me a bad taste in my mouth. There was no demon inside me that had started stirring. You can create new pathways in your brain. It's called neuroplasticity, and it is a beautiful thing. What is dangerous is the thought that you are powerless. That same scenario of getting the wrong drink has happened to other people, but the alleged "slippery slope" is built on half-truths and falsehoods others have told you for a lifetime. *You are cut from a different cloth. There's us and there's them. Normies. You're just one drink away from being a drunk. Etc.*

Empowering someone with curiosity and encouraging them to ask questions after something like that happens such as, *How did it make you feel? Was it what you thought it would be? Did it serve you in any way?* is more powerful than people realize.

This journey is very rarely linear, but it doesn't ever come back to where you are right now. A fellow coach and friend provided a great visual of this process by comparing it to a marathon. When someone runs a marathon and falls, do they have to get up and go back to the starting line? Absolutely not. They get back up and keep moving forward. I've also seen beautiful footage of runners helping another runner who has fallen to get up and then continuing on together. This is what the healing process looks like. Sometimes we fall. We need to learn from that experience in order to move forward. When I fell down and started drinking again, oh boy did it hurt. It was a painful and scary experience, but it was something that needed to happen for me to lean into the reasons it happened and learn from it. So, will you fall down? Maybe. But if you do, you can get back up and resume your journey from where you are; you don't have to go back to the starting line. This is your journey. You'll never know unless you try.

In my book and my coaching, I share a lot of how my health care providers were my partners during my healing process. I encourage you to use that resource as well, but it's going to take some honesty on your part. When you bring them into this process with you, it can be such a beautiful thing. If you don't feel like you can talk to your doctor, then find another one. Be the one who changes their perception of what this process looks like. Have doctors tended to not fully believe a patient when it comes to the topic of drinking? Absolutely. But can we blame them? When someone is lied to frequently, they take their own protective measures.

I recently had to change physicians because my doctor left their clinical practice. I was devastated. She had been such a big part of my story, and there was mutual trust between us that was so important to me. So when I met with my new provider, I spoke about how essential mutual trust is to me. I needed to be honest with her, and in return I needed her to trust and believe me.

Doctors are like investigators—magnifying glass and all. When we struggle, they try to make the connection as to what the problem might be. How can they help us and be our partners in recovery when we hold back pieces of the puzzle?

Your story can change. Your journey can take you down a path you never thought possible. It's time to stop waiting for it to happen, because you are the one holding the key.

Love,
Karla

INTRODUCTION

WHY AM I HERE?

It was 2016. I was sitting in a massive Baptist church in Georgetown, South Carolina, where the weather is typically normal at 100 percent humidity. A friend had asked me to join the community Bible study there. I was a little hesitant about joining because I really didn't like to commit to things for fear of letting people down. However, this was the first time in my life I could join something like this because, for the first time since college, I wasn't at a day job. Plus, my baby girl could happily play down in the childcare room where I'm sure she'd get her fill of apple juice and goldfish. I had heard great things about this place. What could it hurt to temporarily step out of my happy bubble of seclusion? Besides, it was probably only four to six weeks anyway, right?

Boy, was I wrong.

First, I was wrong about the timing. This was not four to six weeks; it lasted the entire school year. What had I gotten myself into? Second, stepping outside of my happy little bubble of solitude was harder than I thought it would be. I got a call from our small group leader who wanted to welcome me to the group. She exuded happiness. Even her name was Joy! She was genuinely excited for me to be in this group and went on about how much fun it would be and how close we would get. Whoa, Joy. Thickening the walls of my bubble I said, "Yeah, that's nice. I'm sure it's great and all, but I'm a really private person and I won't be sharing. Anything."

Joy didn't even sound annoyed. Oh, joy.

On our first day of small groups I was so nervous. Sitting on one of those hard, stackable plastic chairs, I noticed that everyone had their name tag on. I, of course, had forgotten mine and had no idea where it was. I pulled out my workbook that I hadn't even opened yet and wiped the Cheerios crumbles off the paper edges. I was sweating. The only thing I had done right that morning was wear black. At least that would hide the wet spots that were surely forming under my arms. I was scanning the room to see whether I knew anyone, and sure enough, there were a few that I knew "of." Racing thoughts started: *Did they know "of" me? If so, what did they know and what had they heard?* It was hard to concentrate. Ugh, it was going to be a long year.

We were studying Matthew in the Bible that year, and I truly found it fascinating. I found myself loosening up some and even participating … some. The game changer for me was when we got to the parable of the hidden talents (Matthew 25:14–28). In this story, a master was leaving his house and entrusted his property to his servants. Each servant received a certain number of talents; each talent was a substantial amount of money. One servant received five talents, another received two, and a third received one. The first two servants quickly invested their money and doubled what their master had given them. The third decided to dig a hole in the ground and hide his master's money.

My takeaway from this was huge. You see, God gave me this pretty amazing gift—my life. Just over two years before, I was in organ failure, fighting for my life in the hospital. When I got sick, I prayed for another chance. I begged that my time wasn't over yet and swore I'd never drink again. But I also tried to bury my story. I wanted to hide my past and just move forward in life.

I was obedient. I stopped drinking and was honestly doing great. Still, there was this strong message repeating in my mind. I could almost hear it: "I didn't save you so that you could keep it to yourself."

Hiding my story was easy enough to do. I looked healthy, was happily married, and had a beautiful baby girl. Most people hadn't seen the sickness. They hadn't looked into my bright yellow eyes, hadn't seen my yellow-green skin and my pregnant-looking belly so full of fluid. They hadn't seen my muscles so atrophied that I couldn't go from kneeling to standing.

Who wouldn't want to bury all of that? Bury it and breathe a huge sigh of relief that that was over with.

The once-whispered message became louder: "I DIDN'T SAVE YOU SO THAT YOU COULD KEEP IT TO YOURSELF."

There was this tiny flame rising inside me that compelled me to do something with my story. The whisper gave it the oxygen it needed to breathe, live, and grow. I knew I wanted to help people who were scared, just like I was.

But then panic would set in … no, just no. I can't put myself out there again. The wounds from the gossip still felt fresh. Those whispers about me burned and left scars. I trusted no one. Some people recommended that I move away from where I live to avoid the label that would surely attach to me for a lifetime. How in the world could I overtly speak about my past and share it?

Interesting things happen when you've knocked on death's door. After it happened to me, I found a layer of inner strength that wasn't there before—an armor of perspective that shields against more than I could've imagined.

I went from being a self-proclaimed private individual going into that Baptist church, to walking out of there with a business and a blog.

I'm here because my story isn't over. I'm here because you or your loved one's story isn't over either. My intention is to bring to light that you have the power to overcome what might seem hopeless. Maybe my story can ignite a spark in you to get back on your own path—a path toward freedom.

SECTION 1
THE CLIMB

CHAPTER 1

ANXIETY RIDDEN

4
AND SHE CAME TUMBLING DOWN

When I was little, I'd get these night tremors. My entire body would shake and I couldn't get it to stop. I'd crawl into my parents' bed, and my mom would start the routine of having me focus on my toes until they relaxed, then moving up the rest of my body doing the same. If my legs started shaking again by the time we got to my head, back down to the toes we would go and start over again. I remember she was worried and took me to see a doctor, who proceeded to ask if someone was being mean to me at school or if I was worried about something. I could never pinpoint it. Nobody was bullying me, and I didn't *feel* worried about anything, so there were no medical answers at that time. I just self-diagnosed as being … well … different from others.

My body tremors went away for the most part, and I went through the normal internal chaos of middle school years—wanting to be popular but never really fitting in with the popular kids. High school was the same. I was athletically talented, thanks to my dad, so I made the cheerleading squad and was pretty darn good. That's where I made some friendships that I still treasure to this day. Yet high school is also where I can see my anxiety start presenting its ugly head. And by anxiety, I don't mean the everyday what-am-I-going-to-wear-so-I-look-cute-today kind of stuff. It's the stuff that isn't rational and is nearly impossible to talk about with others. The stuff that added to my belief that I was different. <u>That's when I was introduced to shame. And I didn't even know it.</u>

My first panic attack came when I was a freshman in high school watching a college basketball game in a big gymnasium. I can't remember who won the game—heck, I barely remember who I was with—but I vividly remember what happened.

I was sitting way up in the nosebleed section and started to feel a little "off." A wave of unsteadiness came over me, which caused my brain to freak out and start racing with thoughts: *Is there something wrong with me? Am I going to pass out? What if I passed out right here in front of everyone?* Those thoughts were coming at me like a broken record skipping and repeating the same verses over and over. I HAD to get out of there. I tried to stand up, only to have to immediately sit back down because of the dizziness. How was I going to get out of there? My hands became slippery with sweat, and my eyes welled up with tears. So, I did the only thing I knew to do at the time. I slid down those cement stairs one by one on my rear. You can imagine the looks I got from everyone who was watching. I was absorbing their thoughts as though I was a mind reader: *What's wrong with her? She's weird.*

Anxiety and panic attacks have powerful rippling effects. After the butt-slide episode, anxiety slowly weaved its way into all aspects of my life.

When I went to college, my anxiety packed its A game and came with me. I couldn't escape it. Driving the interstate was a nightmare for me. I remember driving up I-85 while white-knuckling the wheel and blasting the AC so I could use the cold air to dry my sweaty hands. Going to the grocery store was another thing that became very difficult for me. Sounds crazy, I know, but worrying about having a panic attack in the grocery store riddled me with fear until I was in my 30s. And worry was just the beginning of the exhausting journey. This was long before the days of Instacart or credit card machines you could just tap on to make transactions. This was back when I only had checks. So, I'd sit in the parking lot and coach myself to go in and just get a few things for the week. I had the store memorized and knew exactly where to go to get what I needed. I knew the longer I was in there, the worse the anxiety would get.

My heart breaks when I look back at myself like that. The mental energy that it took just to buy ramen noodles and some Diet Cokes was absolutely draining. And how do you explain such things to your college roommates? "Yeah … hey, I know you are working on your English essay, but could you help me out with buying some groceries? I can pay for it. I just can't actually go in and do it." Let me tell you, for a 19 year old filled with insecurities, it was crippling. I was a wreck.

Another big component of my anxiety was this tremor that I had in my hands. My hands seemed to shake naturally, and combining anxiety with the shakes was downright embarrassing. It made me extremely self-conscious to do everyday things such as eating and drinking. If I was asked to write something in front of people … forget it. I'll never forget my statistics class at Clemson. At the beginning of class, the professor would have us write the answers to the homework questions on the chalkboard. He would randomly assign the questions, and up to the front of the room we would go to write out our work. This was almost impossible for me to do. By the time the professor would call on me to go up, I was shaking so bad I could barely hold my pencil and paper, let alone go up and write on the board. Many times I'd tell him I couldn't do it, and he'd assume I didn't do my work. But I did do my work, and it was right (mostly due to my amazing statistics tutor)! One day before class, I decided to ask my teacher if I could go ahead and start writing one of the homework questions on the board before the other students got there. He was confused, but he was fine with it. So every week I'd rearrange my schedule so I could go into class early to write a problem on the board. This helped my grade, but it only added to my shame. People would come in and look at me finishing up at the chalkboard, and my mind-reading capabilities would kick in again. What I assumed they were thinking about me was what my inner critic was yelling at me all the time: *There's something wrong with you! You'll never fit in! You're such an embarrassment!*

What happened in my statistics class is a visual of how I started rearranging my life around my anxiety. The anxiety came first, and then I'd come up with ways to try to avoid it or at least make it less painful. The process was exhausting.

An additional manifestation of my anxiety also started in college where public speaking was a requirement. This one carried a heavy load of shame with it. (Man, that anxiety and shame sure doesn't travel lightly.) Just hearing the two words *public speaking* would send me into a tailspin that was hard to see through. I had to do it, though. I was already carrying the memory of having given one speech that left me tongue-tied, shaking, and leaving the room never to come back. Though I lucked out and got a class that was really small compared to others, my anxiety didn't seem to care. On the day of my first speech, I was in full panic mode. I left the classroom and headed to the bathroom in the hallway, desperate to rid myself of this feeling. I needed it OUT. So, I stuck my fingers down my throat and threw up. And I actually felt better. I immediately went back to the room and delivered my five-minute speech. I didn't have to run out of the room, and I wasn't in full body shakes, so I saw all of this as success. Unfortunately, my brain did too. It formed a new neural pathway that told me, "Hey, if you're feeling really anxious, puking makes you feel better." This progressed quickly, and over the years I didn't need to stick my fingers down my throat at all—it came automatically.

Great, so now I was the shaky girl that puked a lot. Perfect.

Anxiety needs a different name. One that describes the exhaustion and fear that it causes. One that describes the ugly web it weaves through life.

I went to many counselors but didn't get much help. There are so many good counselors out there. Unfortunately, I didn't find a good one until I was in my 30s, so I was in for a long, lonely journey. I went to see a neurologist about my shaky hands. I was convinced I had a brain tumor or something extremely deadly, so you can imagine my anxiety was having a heyday with that. I remember sitting on the exam table, feeling the crunch of the table paper under my legs, bracing myself for the bad news. When the doctor came in, he simply asked, "Do your tremors stop when you drink alcohol?" I became excited because the answer was a clear YES; they stopped almost immediately when I drank. He must understand exactly what this is! I'll get fixed! The next words that he uttered stuck with me for years: "Well then, just drink a beer or two and you'll be fine.

Just don't drink too much." And with that, he left the room—along with my excitement that promptly deflated like a balloon.

You see, I was already worried about my drinking. Not because I was this huge partier and drank all the time—I wasn't—but because of two main factors. First, my parents had warned us as kids that alcoholism ran in our family. Both sets of grandparents "had it" and it was genetic. All I knew was that I did NOT want "that" thing. It sounded horrific. I really believed it was something that you either had or didn't have. Second, I wasn't really worried about the amount I was drinking. Heck, I was in college, and that's where you're *supposed* to drink. It was part of the experience. Everyone drank. I was more worried about how much I counted on it to help me. In a world where I felt different and weird, alcohol made me feel normal. I thought it was what helped the "real me" come out. It whispered to my soul that it was the answer to my need for calm.

Alcohol lied to me.

CHAPTER 2

THE BEST LAID PLANS

I think I knew deep down that alcohol was lying to me, but I didn't really want to know the truth. I mean, have you noticed how popular alcohol is? It's everywhere, and it's invited to all the events.

In college, I thought if I just pushed harder and kept busy, I would kick anxiety to the curb and then I wouldn't need alcohol. My senior year of college I had a part time job, and I was taking 21 hours of classes each week. I had transferred to Clemson my sophomore year of school, and in doing so I had lost a lot of credits. But I was determined to graduate on time. Looking back, I can see that I thought if I could just run from it fast enough I would grow out of it somehow. I was wrong.

I mentioned earlier that when I left to go to college, my anxiety packed its A game. Well, by the time I left college, it must have joined a sorority because it ended up bringing all of its new, anxious friends home with us.

While I was at Clemson, my parents had moved to the coast of SC, so I moved there while I looked for a job. I always thought the beach was going to be a temporary place for me, but it's where I live to this day. I found a job at a brand-new wellness facility that actually let me use my degree in Health Science. I was there for four years when I got the amazing opportunity to interview with a highly respected pharmaceutical company. I'll never forget getting a call from them asking if I could fly to Atlanta, GA, to interview. I was so naive to how the corporate world worked; I remember saying, "Ma'am, I don't think I can afford a plane ticket right now." The woman paused, and then said, "Miss, we will be taking care of the ticket and flying you to Atlanta to interview." Well, you could have picked my jaw up off the floor. Wow! They were going to fly *me* to Atlanta.

I was walking on clouds and filled with excitement—until I walked into the area of the airport where they were conducting the interviews and saw hundreds of people lined up in their best business suits. My cloud-walking balloon quickly deflated and crippling anxiety filled the space. What was I going to do? Then I remembered I had a tool for that. I immediately went to the bathroom and got sick. I then waited in that painfully long line and tried to calm my nerves until my name was called. I made sure to know where the bathrooms were located just in case the anxiety built up too much again. Nobody had a clue about the internal hell I was in. I had become a pro at hiding it.

I nailed my interview. For me, the anxiety is all about the buildup; the wait was torture for me. As I was leaving, one of the managers asked me to stay for more interviews. It was such an amazing feeling. Nobody saw the girl who was trembling in the bathroom sticking her finger down her throat to calm her nerves. When I finished the other interviews, my high was back. I knew I had done well. My first stop at the airport was the bar for a celebratory glass of wine. I deserved it after all of that, right?

<u>I kept thinking that if my life changed—if I got a good job, got out of a bad relationship, or stopped living paycheck to paycheck—my anxiety would go away and I would drink less.</u> I did end up getting the job with the pharmaceutical company and I thought, *This is it. This is my time to change.*

I had to go to training for eight weeks in Atlanta. Oh, I had so many plans. I was going to eat well, I would exercise regularly, and I wasn't going to drink much. This company was known for its intense training program. Trainees had to complete multiple tests per week with a score of 90 percent or above to pass, and the company had a strict three-strikes-and-you're out policy.

Everyone at training stayed at the same long-stay hotel. This particular hotel had a free happy hour every day from 4–6 p.m. with all the wine you could drink. So as soon as we finished class each day, a big group of us would go back to the hotel and start filling our cups with the cheap red wine. When it would get close to 6 p.m., we'd fill our biggest cup and go hit the books. How I retained any information is beyond me. I did well on the tests, but I was a basket case.

All the trainers warned us to save a fail for the last test because it centered around laws in pharma and the medical community. It was the last week of training. I was exhausted. All of my initial plans for the eight weeks of eating well, exercising, and not drinking much were out the window. Instead, my fellow coworkers and I crammed for tests and got little sleep. That last week I took my law test, my hands were shaking when I hit the submit button. As I watched the little hourglass on the screen spin as the computer calculated my score, I felt like I was going to puke. Then a big 88 came up on the screen. FAIL. I was so lucky that this was my very first fail of the entire eight weeks. I watched as others weren't so lucky. They were being escorted out of the training center and sent home. I had gotten to know these people. Many had families back at home depending on them to get this job. I was single and 25 years old. Nobody was counting on my paycheck but me. I broke down in tears and started sobbing uncontrollably. The trainer was looking at me as though I'd lost my marbles. I imagined she was thinking, *Why are you crying? You haven't failed any tests yet. You'll be fine.* But it was so much more than that. My nervous system was shot. I was exhausted both physically and intellectually. I don't know whether there are more layers than that, but if there are, I was exhausted at those levels too. Still the message I kept telling myself was, *Keep pushing forward. Keep pushing and things will get better.*

I had so much going for me. I had a great job and I bought my first house by the time I was 26. But I was insanely anxious. Alcohol was still helping, but not as much as it used to, so I started drinking more.

It was my relationships. Yes, that had to be it. Maybe if I fixed that, things would change and I would get a break from this world of panic.

CHAPTER 3

PINK ICE

Looking back, it's not surprising I had no agency for myself. I started to feel less than, or different from others even before I was butt-sliding down those stadium stairs in a panic back in high school. Sadly, darkness can come into your world dressed like a white knight. When I was in the first grade, we moved from Kansas to Columbia, SC. We attended an Episcopal church for several years, and when I was 11, it was expected that my sisters and I would attend youth group. The youth director was fun and cool, and the parents were thrilled because they didn't have to force their kids to go back to church on Sunday night for group because they were actually looking forward to it. Over the years, not only did he woo the kids, he

SADLY, DARKNESS CAN COME INTO YOUR WORLD DRESSED LIKE A WHITE KNIGHT.

was there for all of the parents as well. He became a family friend, and someone we all trusted. I'm not sure if these were the years they didn't do background checks on people, or if it was because his father was a big wig at the church, but unbeknownst to the parents, they were sending their children to a predator that already had an arrest record involving children and sexual behavior. His eagerness to help, and willingness to provide us a shoulder to cry on was only his way of grooming his prey. By the time I was in middle school, he had exposed me to porn, and even though I had repeatedly said no to anything physical, he didn't give up. We moved away for a year when I was 12 years old, due to a change in jobs for my dad, and I remember thinking that the one positive thing about the temporary move was that I would rid myself of this monster. I was wrong. And that's when the phone calls started. He would call when he knew I was home alone from school and ask me to talk about things to help arouse him. I would internally beat myself up. *Just hang up the phone and don't answer.* It seemed like such a simple task. The internal battle was a full-blown war. He was a church leader. He was my dad's friend. Everyone loved him. *What's wrong with me?* When we moved back to Columbia, SC after that year, the phone calls continued, and if I didn't answer, he would soon be parked on the street in front of our house. The torment finally came to a stop when my eldest sister overheard me talking to my other sister, trying to come up with a strategic plan to deflect his advances. Just writing that breaks my heart. We thought we were so grown, but we were about 12 and 13 at the time, trying to tackle something no child should ever have to. My sister immediately told our mother, who immediately hid the car keys, and then told my father. The police were called and our abuser was arrested. This is when they found out about the prior arrests and all the evidence they needed to confirm our story. Unfortunately, we had to go through court, where the defense attorney repeated the self-destructive thoughts I had had for so long: *Why didn't you just hang up the phone or not answer?* He added an extra jab. *You must have wanted it.* It was a stab that went so deep that later, no matter how much therapy I had, his words haunted me.

 The judge ordered the former youth director to house arrest and therapy. We weren't the only children that he had preyed on; we were just the only ones that came forward. He also had to pay for my sister and I to get a certain amount of therapy from an appointed therapist. By the time it was all over, I was so over talking about it. I was fine. I just wanted to get over it and move on. It was a tactic I continued to use throughout my life: Push it away and keep moving forward. I eventually learned that's not how the body works.

⊷ ⊷ ⊷ ⊷ ⊷

I had a highschool sweetheart who was nice, but that relationship came to an end when he handed me a card between classes one day at school. I thought the card was going to be a declaration of his love for me, or at least an invitation to see if I wanted to go to Taco Bell after school. I mean, he had just given me a pink ice ring for Christmas—that was serious. Instead, the front of the card depicted a frog sitting on a lily pad, and inside it read, "I feel like pond scum." He broke up with me. Ah, the innocence of those days.

I went from pink ice rings and fun dates to bruised arms from a guy who would grab me so hard when he was angry. It was like a culture shock. One time, he punched a hole in the wall right by my head after I found out he had been cheating on me. And I still didn't leave.

In college, I dated a guy who was nice and didn't drink at all. I still remember my 21st birthday—he was helping me stumble back to the car and I ultimately got sick behind some dumpster. Classy. He looked at me and said, "Why would you want to drink something that makes you sick?" It was such a simple question. I remember thinking, *Gosh, this guy is clueless.* I mean, we were in college. You're supposed to party when you're in college. I just drank too much. Looking back, this guy was spot on. I just had no idea and wouldn't figure it out for a long time.

My relationships continued to run through cycles of cheating and my drinking just continued. There was never a thought of stopping, just making plans to slow down. From the outside looking in, it must have looked crazy. Why wouldn't I just get out of it? I know it was painful for others to watch and it impacted my relationships with my family and friends. I was slowly disconnecting from people.

There was always an excuse. *I'll take a break after the holidays. I'll stop for a while after that wedding. I'll make a plan to cut back after that work trip. This relationship is the reason I'm drinking so much, so I'll cut back when I get out of it.* There was always something.

Looking back, I see there was a huge part of my life when chunks of time were passing by. I always had a plan to stop after an event or situation. Meanwhile, my body was growing weary.

There was always an excuse.

- THE HOLIDAYS
- A WEDDING
- DINNER WITH YOUR IN-LAWS
- YOUR BIRTHDAY
- VACATION

PINK ICE 19

GOING ON A DATE

SUPERBOWL

FRIENDS VISITING FROM OUT OF TOWN

WINE TASTING EXCURSION

WORK HAPPY HOUR

MOTHER'S DAY

NEW YEAR'S EVE

EASTER EGG HUNT

BABY SHOWER

"GIRLS NIGHT OUT"

ANOTHER WEDDING

CAMPING TRIP

"I'll take a break after the Holidays... I will stop for a while after that wedding... I will make a plan to cut back after that work trip..."

CHAPTER 4

THE DOWNWARD SPIRAL

As weary as I was, I still blamed my exhaustion solely on anxiety. When I was 28, I still felt invincible, doing well at work, and "pushing through" life like a champ. This is when things took a turn for the worse.

I was out with a group of friends one night. Toward the end of the evening, I couldn't stand or walk straight. This really wasn't typical for me. I didn't know up from down; it was a horrible feeling. A friend offered to help me get to my room, and I only have a few flashes of what happened from there; me pushing on his head, and the texture of his hair. Did I tell him to stop? Did I say I wanted it? I remember waking up the next day still dressed in what I was wearing the night before, but only from the top up; my jeans were laying on the floor. Panic washed over me. I knew something had happened because I felt a dull pain between my legs. I thought he was my friend. The shame was almost unbearable. I quickly got dressed, determined to ignore or push away whatever had happened that night. *That's what you get, Karla, for drinking too much.* I didn't even want to put the pieces of the puzzle together. Like, why couldn't I walk at the end of the night? Had my drink been spiked? I didn't care. It was all my fault. I just needed to push forward and forget about it. Act like it didn't happen.

I would soon learn that our bodies don't easily forget those kinds of things. As much as we want to push traumatic events away, our bodies hold on and keep a tally. The "friend" that I had for over a decade disappeared and we never spoke again. He knew what he had done. But the only person I blamed was myself.

The one thing that got off scot-free that night was alcohol. Not once did it cross my mind that alcohol disempowered me that night. But it makes sense, since the first thing alcohol impacts is the prefrontal cortex of the brain, which controls so many things, including decision making. Not just mine, but also his. Nope, alcohol just came off as the golden child that was there by my side to pick up the pieces. I was shattered.

My panic was at an all-time high. I just wanted to numb it out, so my drinking intensified. I would drink at night and then be up at 3 a.m. scrubbing the kitchen from top to bottom. It's like I was manic.

I reached out for help from my company and told them I was struggling. During a conversation with the wellness coordinator, she asked me if I had an issue with drinking. I said yes, but that it was because of my anxiety; anxiety was my issue, not alcohol. She said, "You mean to tell me you would rather me write down that you have mental health issues than alcohol addiction?" I was desperately trying to protect that precious liquid. It was the only thing that offered me solace during hard times! Nothing else worked. I knew that admitting I struggled with alcohol meant that I could never drink again.

So I told myself that if all of the stress would just stop, I'd be able to control my drinking. *Maybe if I could just take a break from my world of chaos, I could kick this thing.* The only way I knew how to do that was to get help and go away somewhere. As much as it scared me, the thought of just stopping work, emails, bills, and my current toxic relationship—just hitting the pause button—appealed to me.

So off to rehab I went. I told very few people where I was going. I was so grateful to my parents for financially supporting my decision. I was actually excited to go; I wanted to disappear from my world. I also knew it was the only way to stop this downward spiral that I was in. Turns out, that was about all rehab did for me.

I felt better as soon as the alcohol was out of my system. I did everything the rehab team told me to do; I was an A+ rehab student. I followed all the rules, and went to a nauseating number of Alcoholics Anonymous (which hereafter will refer to as AA) meetings. Each meeting I went to reinforced to me that I didn't attach to this disease thing, and I didn't identify as being an "alcoholic," powerless in my addiction. It was mostly meetings that I had to go to, but I also met with addiction specialists a few times. One told me I was not only an alcoholic, but I also had an eating disorder because of my throwing up. I remember asking the therapist, "How do I have an eating disorder when my getting sick has nothing to do with food or eating?" Hell, I love food. I'm just nervous. I was told the sooner I came to terms with my powerlessness to these things, the sooner I would get better.

You are powerless. You have to change your group of friends. You can't be around alcohol. You have a disease. Oh and it cost a lot of money. That's what I left with.

I sure did feel better physically, though.

We live in a society where two things come to mind when someone is struggling with alcohol: AA and rehab. People think those are the only ways to get better. This is simply not true. The rise in alcohol related health issues should have people questioning that belief. Telling someone they are powerless over something, then releasing them unequipped into a world where temptation beckons at every corner and alcohol is glamorized on TV screens and social media simply doesn't work. You can't white-knuckle your way through life. That only works temporarily. Rehab is needed to help monitor people coming off a substance. While studies show only about ten percent of individuals are physically addicted to alcohol, detox is something to take seriously. Going to a rehabilitation center can be necessary to stop someone's spiral.

Speaking of spirals, mine continued aggressively. My job with the pharmaceutical company ended when they went through one of their big layoffs and I was part of the cut. It was a huge blow to me, because I had wrapped up so much of my personal value in my career. I didn't worry about money; unfortunately I also didn't save it. With the layoff came a severance package which bought me some time. Of course, "Little Miss Fix-It" showed up and I told myself *now* I will finally get better. My days will be open and free of stress, so I can workout, eat healthy, and cut back on drinking (yeah, I know it sounds familiar). Sadly, not working meant there were no boundaries determining when I could start drinking. I slept in each day and tumbled around on the hamster wheel of shame and blame which was stronger than ever before. I was depressed and my anxiety was debilitating. I finally got a new job, and I was excited about it. I was going to be a physician liaison which was right in my wheelhouse. In this role, I would introduce new physicians to existing physicians or those they would most likely be referring their patients to. I would get to continue working with physicians, but this new job also came with a dramatic pay cut. I received my tax returns from the pharmaceutical company the same day I got my offer from my new employer and all I could do was break down and cry. I was going to be facing some major changes to my livelihood. I thought things couldn't get any worse.

Unfortunately, the roller coaster I was on only included steep drops.

CHAPTER 5

YELLOW

To many, the color yellow represents happiness or enlightenment. Some may even think of basking in the warm sun on a summer day. Me? I've never been quite sure how I feel about yellow.

Life keeps coming at you whether your world is falling apart or not. My anxiety became a part of my identity. It's just who I was and how I was wired, so I lived my life around it. Same with the shaky hands. I found all kinds of ways to hide those trembling digits of mine. If I had a business lunch, ordering soup was a no-no, as was signing the check or writing anything in front of people. It was taxing. The message from the neurologist was etched in my memory. Yes, alcohol instantly helped the primary tremors, but I felt like I was watching alcohol weave its way through the ins and outs of my life just like anxiety did. It was getting crowded. Didn't anyone understand what this was like?

The scary thing about alcohol is that it's not just socially acceptable, it's socially expected. It's everywhere, and that made me feel normal.

Yellow can be a sign of deception.

I saw many therapists about my anxiety. Interestingly, they never asked about my drinking. To be honest, if they had, I wouldn't have told the truth about it anyway. People didn't understand how much it helped me, so I'd downplay it. I knew that when people say they struggle with alcohol, the first thing that happens is they get labeled and told they can never drink again. So if I could just fix this anxiety, my alcohol intake would decrease.

I was prescribed medications for anxiety several times but didn't feel like they worked. Looking back, I realize that I didn't really give them a shot because I'm sure the alcohol lessened their efficacy. I even got to the point where I didn't want to take any pills because, deep down, I was afraid of mixing medications and alcohol. I was starting to wonder whether I was trying to deceive other people or myself.

Each day took so much energy to "pull off." I wanted everything to be okay. I could fix it. I was getting so tired. But just to be sure I was A-okay in the alcohol department, I'd go to the most dependable place out there for answers: Google.

Yellow can mean sickness.

The internet was my safe place. I could Google anything I wanted and Google wouldn't judge me. "What are the signs of drinking too much?" "What is an alcoholic?" "Am I an alcoholic?" I wonder how many times I asked my computer friend these questions. I'm not sure what I thought I was going to do with the answers. It could easily make me feel better because I could name several people in my life who'd qualify as having a problem just like I did. So I wasn't any different. "Does alcohol make my face red?" and "What are the signs of liver issues?" were questions I'd type into my search engine late at night. Those things caused me more anxiety, and there was one tool that worked for that … Yep, alcohol.

My Google searches are where I learned about jaundice. Jaundice causes a yellowing of the skin and whites of the eyes caused by the buildup of bilirubin in the blood. I had no clue exactly what all of that meant, but I knew it was associated with the liver. So that's when I randomly started checking the whites of my eyes in the rearview mirror when I'd get into my car in the morning. But I didn't need to worry about that, because I wasn't one of *those* kinds of people.

Yellow can mean caution.

I'd just put some rules around my drinking. Yes, that would fix it. Even simply thinking about that felt like setting down a weight. I felt empowered.

I had rules such as, drinking only on the weekends, drinking only between 5 and 8 p.m., and drinking water between each alcoholic beverage. I'd give it up for Lent, just to prove to myself that I didn't have a problem. <u>Whenever I did give it up, my body would show me how much it appreciated it.</u> My eyes were happy, my skin was clear, I dropped a few pounds, and (a little TMI here) going to the bathroom felt amazing! Unfortunately, at the end of those 40 days I'd feel so great that I'd go back to it to … well … celebrate. Because you celebrate with alcohol, right?

I was burning out.

I read somewhere that burnout is nature's way of telling you that while you've been going through the motions, your soul has started to depart. I deeply resonate with this. I was so busy spinning plates and pretending that nothing was wrong with me that I never noticed I was losing my soul. Little did I know at that time that I was close to losing my physical body as well.

Yellow can mean danger.

I didn't know what it was like to feel good anymore. I'd see specialists about health concerns, again never bringing up my drinking and never being challenged on my answer that I drank a "few" glasses of wine a night. One day, I *finally* got the nerve to be honest with my doctor about my drinking. I made and canceled the appointment at least three times before I finally showed up.

The wait for the doctor was excruciating. When he came in and asked me what he could help me with that day, I blurted out, "I'm here because I'm scared about my drinking. I'm worried, and I'm just so anxious. I don't know what to do." Ahh, deep breath out. I did it. I said it. Mission accomplished. But the doctor lightheartedly said, "Don't we all!" I could almost hear the beeping sound of a truck backing up. I wanted to put all my words back in my mouth. I never went back to that doctor.

I was stuck and I was scared. I tried everything. I was fearful of having withdrawals if I did try to stop. I was reeling with these scary thoughts.

I was anxious. I was tired. I was alone.

But I also thought I'd get a little better and fix it.

Thankfully, things started to improve for me. My personal life took an upswing when I got into a healthy relationship and finally got out from under the mortgage for a house that was financially draining me. Ahh. *Things are going to get better*, I thought. *I feel like I can breathe.*

Then one day as I climbed into my car, I checked my rearview mirror to take a peek at my eyes. My stomach dropped to my feet. My hands shook. There it was, clear as day: yellow.

Yellow can mean fear.

CHAPTER 6

AND THEN SHE CAME TUMBLING DOWN

Now what? What was I going to do?

At this time in my life, I was 37 years old, had never been married, didn't have kids, and was dating the kindest man I'd ever met in my life—Grady. I was so scared to talk to anyone about my concerns, even Grady. Looking back, I was probably more afraid to talk to him because he was a physician. I had this idea that physicians only think one way about this topic, and that would mean I'd be sent off to meetings where I needed to proclaim my powerlessness. But it didn't matter anymore. He was surely going to leave me anyway. Who in their right mind would stay? The shame was suffocating.

I actually participated in a wedding the very weekend I saw the dreaded yellow in my eyes. I still can't believe I went and did it. But I lived in an unhealthy, people-pleasing mindset at the time, so telling my friend I couldn't be in her wedding was something I categorized as a thing you just can't do. I mean, who does that? So even though my body was begging me to stop, I kept pushing forward. I'd tell myself, *Just get through it and then ask for help*. Just writing about it now brings back the weariness I felt back then.

The night before the wedding, I confided in a dear friend who was also a physician. Even all these years later, I can still hear her calm tone and her true concern and care. It was exactly what I needed. Together, she and Grady planned to take me to a local emergency room in Charleston, SC the next day.

I just wanted to sleep.

I was not prepared for the whirlwind of chaos that happened once we got to the emergency room. I could see the worry in people's eyes. My spinning plates began crashing down, and my body started shutting down. I noticed my arm was a strange color, like a weird tan. I explained to the nurse that I had used self-tanner for the wedding that weekend, trying to justify the cause of the strange hue. I remember her looking at me with annoyance while saying, "I hate to tell you, sweetie, but that's not tanning cream. That's your liver."

Ouch. Raw truth stings. So I just covered myself with my comfort blanket of shame.

All the control that I'd been trying to hang onto was slipping through my fingers.

I was taken by ambulance to the Medical University of South Carolina. I could feel the sense of urgency coming from the staff. Clearly I was deathly ill, but all I could think was, *What are people going to think?* Though I feel sorry for how I was back then, it was all I knew to think at the time.

After a day or so of many tests, I was released from the hospital with the promise that I'd come back for blood work a few days later. I had this huge sense of relief. Okay. Time to get some control back. *Now* I was going to fix things. Surely my body would get right back on track since I wasn't drinking.

I had no idea what I was in for.

A few days later, I did as promised. My calm, caring friend took me to get blood work. The looks I saw from the people at the local lab were of shock and worry. I looked horrible. My skin was the color of an Oompa Loompa from the original *Charlie and the Chocolate Factory*, with a little yellow and green mixed in. The size of my belly had grown so tremendously that I had to borrow my dad's stretchy t-shirts and pants. I had no idea what was going on, I just knew it wasn't good and I wanted to sleep. The time between getting my blood taken and the chilling phone call that came next is truly a blur.

I was sleeping when I got a call on my cell phone. I recognized the number was coming from Charleston, so I reluctantly answered.

"Is this Karla Kephart? Ms. Kephart, are you okay? How are you feeling?" I could hear the worry and urgency in the physician's voice.

I responded, "I feel so bad. I just can't wake up. I think I'm dying."

"Ms. Kephart ... I think you are too."

She said some other words after that. Something about getting my lab results. It all sounded like Charlie Brown's teacher talking on the other end. What did she just say? I'm dying? My world began to move in painful slow motion.

The last thing I heard the physician say was, "Ms. Kephart, do you have transportation to get here? If not, I will send an ambulance to come get you."

Another wave of panic washed over me. Send an ambulance to get me? Was this actually happening? Sitting on the couch and wrapped in a blanket, I stared in disbelief. It was almost as though I was staring at the tiny, shattered pieces of all the plates I'd been spinning for years. There would be no more scrambling to fix this. What had I done?

I immediately called my dad. I can't imagine getting a call like that from my child. He said he and my mom would be right over. Thank goodness my parents lived close. I also called Grady, who promptly left work to come get me and take me to Charleston.

As I was sitting there trying to process what was happening, my dad and I had a powerful exchange of words.

"Daddy, she said I was dying. What if I die?"

He very calmly said, "<u>Karla, yes, you could die, but you could also live. I want you to think about living right now.</u>"

It was a brief glimpse of hope.

The next few weeks were a waiting game of seeing whether my body would start working again.

I was in acute liver failure, which is loss of liver function that happens rapidly—within days or weeks. One thing that became painfully clear to me was that the liver is this crazy important organ that we can't live without. Toxins were flooding my body. I couldn't go to the bathroom because everything inside me just stopped moving. When I could urinate, it was the color of beef broth. To this day, I can't look at beef broth without being reminded of those days.

The nights were so long and scary. The beeping noises were unrelenting. The "what ifs" slipped inside my mind, causing panic to set in. I was hooked up to the constant drip of fluids with a needle taped onto my arm to keep the IV pump in place.

My favorite nurse was Connie, who was amazing. Her skin was a dark chocolate color and her voice had a strong Southern drawl. I had the sense that she'd been on this unit for many years because she knew her stuff, and she meant business. Connie was kind to me. She helped me feel safe. One night I looked at her and said, "Connie, I'm just so scared." She pulled me in as close as she could and said, "Baby, I know you are. Let's pray together."

I remembered hearing a story years earlier about someone who had passed away from liver failure. He was in the hospital and couldn't eat. His friend who told me the story was so sad and frustrated. "Why wouldn't he just eat? It could have saved his life." I thought the same thing. Surely if it was a matter of life or death, I would eat, for goodness' sake. Well, here I was with my life on the line and I couldn't eat. The nurses tried bringing me Ensure® and other nutritional shakes, but it just wasn't happening. I had a different understanding now of what that man had gone through. I felt hopeless. How could I fight to live if I couldn't even eat an egg? Later on I learned there are a few reasons for this. Part of the reason I couldn't eat was because of the presence of ascites. The extra fluid in the abdominal compartment compresses the stomach and there is no room for food. The other reason is the inflammation from the liver. This shuts down the appetite in many people. Finally, another reason is due to the circulating toxins not cleared by the liver.

My relationship with my family had been strained for years. It's understandable. It had been hard for them to watch my self destructive behavior. One day, there was a knock on my hospital door. To my surprise, it was my sisters. They had received a call about how serious things were and decided to jump in the car to come see their baby sister. They knew how scared and anxious

I was, so they had put together an iPod playlist that I could listen to. They were worried and confused, and since they lived over three hours away, they didn't want to wait for the call that my condition was declining fast and then not have the chance to make it to me in time.

I couldn't help but notice the look of fear on their faces when they saw me. Despite their best efforts to wear their bravest faces, the fear showed through. How could they not be scared? They weren't prepared to see me look the way I did.

The Medical University of South Carolina is a teaching institute, so whenever you see a physician, you're likely going to see a team of residents following, listening, and taking notes. For a person lying there with her armor of shame on, it was a nightmare. I'd hear them coming down the hall and discussing my chart while they were just outside the door. As someone who was desperate for people *not* to talk about me, it was excruciating to be in a setting where that was a regular occurrence. Several times a day, people would ask me, "How much were you drinking a day?" I'd answer with the same generic response: "Several drinks." They would just ask again. It became so frustrating that I just wanted to yell back, "I don't f***ing know!" And that was the truth. I had no idea; I didn't count. Heck, I'd gotten good at hiding it from even myself.

I tried to hide my drinking in many ways. I didn't want to see how much I had the day before. If I drank wine, I'd switch from a bottle of wine to a box of wine. I'd go to different liquor stores so that the workers didn't see me as a frequent shopper. When I was there, I'd buy just one bottle because it would look bad if I bought more. It was a constant shuffle. I was playing a game of hide-and-seek— and I was losing.

One day, as I was lying in my hospital bed, a resident came in and started pressing on my belly, saying the words that set me into a full panic: "Yep, she will be a transplanter."

Wait ... what? I asked him what he was talking about.

He said, "A transplanter. You are probably going to need a liver transplant." He said it as plainly and matter-of-factly as a plumber tells someone they need a new toilet.

Meanwhile, you could've knocked me over with a feather. I was so thankful Grady was there. He recognized the panic on my face and immediately told the resident he needed to step out of the room. Those who know Grady, know it takes a lot for him to show any form of anger. When he's not at work, Grady doesn't usually pull the "I'm a doctor" card. However, he went out in the hallway, identified himself as a physician, and had a collegial attending-to-attending chat with the resident's supervising physician and requested that the resident be removed from my case, which was granted. I still don't know whether Grady realizes how much that meant to me.

After the doctors performed a paracentesis, my liver finally showed some signs of improving and I was able to slowly start eating. Paracentesis, or an abdominal tap, is when fluid buildup in your belly is removed. In that first procedure, doctors removed over three liters of fluid. I felt like I could breathe again. My belly had been growing the way it had because of a condition called ascites—swelling of the abdomen caused by a buildup of excess fluid. Ascites occurs because of elevated pressure in a major vein that leads to the liver, a situation called portal hypertension. I was so thankful for some improvement, but I was far from out of the woods.

The physicians and residents I encountered during my hospital stay each responded to me differently. The good ones definitely outweighed the bad. I really struggled with the tenured physicians. I felt like they looked down on me as though I was just one more pathetic drunk, as if they expected me to fail. Looking back, though, I see them through a different lens. Physicians tell people all the time that they can get better if they do just one thing, such as stop drinking alcohol. Then their patients don't do it. Doctors go to extreme lengths to save people's lives, and then they find out that their patients go out and do the one thing they were told not to do anymore. How extremely frustrating for them.

I also had physicians who poured their care into me. They took time to educate me. Dr. Jophlin, who was a resident at the time but is now a hepatologist specializing in the liver, explained my situation as the perfect storm happening in the worst way. I was drinking entirely too much, was highly stressed out, and was developing underlying autoimmune issues. I was basically throwing gasoline (alcohol) on burning embers (inflammation). I learned everyone processes alcohol differently. Doctors have seen people present with hepatitis, an inflammation of the liver, just from having two glasses of wine a night. They have also seen people basically pickle themselves with alcohol and yet still walk around somewhat functional. The bottom line is, extreme health risks can happen to anyone who drinks alcohol.

Each day at the hospital I'd have bloodwork done to see how my liver was functioning. These tests measured my liver enzymes (AST and ALT), Bilirubin, and my INR (blood clotting function). Once my numbers started improving, I was finally able to go home. I thought I'd feel excited. Unfortunately, hopelessness started to set in and I just felt depressed. One young physician doing my discharge work must have picked up on how deflated I felt. He simply said, "You know you can do this, right?" Those words snapped me into attention. He said it again: "You can do this. I can tell you have it in you." His words gave me the spark of hope that I desperately needed. At that moment, I swore I was going to come back one day and tell him I had succeeded.

I haven't been able to do that yet, but when I was looking back at my labs in preparation for writing this book, I made it a point to find his name. I'm still excited about telling him that I made it, so I'll find him soon and send him a copy of this book with my thanks. Words make an impact.

Unfortunately, I had to fall down again first. And it was going to be painful.

CHAPTER 7

THE TILTING OF HEADS AND BLESSING OF HEARTS

Here in the South, people love to say, "Bless their heart!" To the uninitiated, it may sound caring, but the well-indoctrinated know that the phrase can have multiple meanings. In my experience, when someone tilts their head to the side and says, "Aww, bless your heart," it means something like, "Aww, you're pathetic." There have been many times I wanted to tilt their head right back in place and tell them to go take a hike. Now don't get me wrong, there are some people who mean it nicely, and when they say they are praying for you, they are legitimately on their hands and knees praying for you to get well. There's always those few, though, and those who have experienced it know exactly what I'm talking about.

Little did I know that surviving the hospital was only my first hurdle to get over. Some of the hardest were yet to come. The physical stuff was challenging. I had been in the hospital for almost two weeks, and lying in a hospital bed for that long took a major toll on my body. Even though I had the paracentesis, my belly was still huge. Because my liver still wasn't working properly, the fluid continued to build up. I would go on to have the paracentesis done several times to remove the fluid. It was always such a relief to have that procedure done. It would take physical pressure off my organs, and I'd be able to eat properly, but it also helped emotionally in a big way. It was hard to look at myself. My body had morphed into something I didn't recognize, and my coloring was still a sickly yellow.

I really wasn't prepared for the emotional stuff. My inner critic was screaming at me non-stop and my "just push through it" mentality was in protective mode. It wanted to clean up the massive mess that had been made and move on like nothing had happened. But that wouldn't be so easily done. I was already hearing that people were talking about me. Listen, I get it. I really do. What happened to me was a pretty juicy story. I remember how hearing stories about other people and their drinking made me feel better about my own drinking. The comparison game is dangerous no matter how you play it, I will say, I was forever changed by being on the receiving end of the gossip.

The first big blow was when I got an email from work saying I needed to come to a meeting at 5:00 p.m. on a Friday. We all know a 5:00 p.m. Friday meeting is NOT good. I remember that drive like it was yesterday. The fear was suffocating. I pulled out one of my old tricks, turning the AC on high and cooling my hands like I used to do in college. There was no alcohol to numb the panic. I was going to have to walk into that meeting feeling everything. A panel of people were there waiting on me. "Ms. Kephart, there are rumors that your sickness was due to drugs and alcohol, so there is a phlebotomist waiting in the other room ready to draw your blood and collect a urine sample to test for drugs." Wham. It almost took my breath away. I felt so small. Anything else they said was just garbled words after that because I couldn't hear it. Any hope of trying to control the narrative was out the window. I obediently went off to give them my samples, not once thinking of standing up for myself. The shame made every step of the way so heavy.

My medical leave was extended until doctors said I could go back. I spent my days trying to go for small walks to build up my strength. Because my bilirubin was still high, my skin itched so bad I wanted to crawl right out of it. The itching woke me up in the middle of the night and nothing seemed to help. When your liver is sick, it doesn't turn over the bilirubin the way it normally does, so it circulates in the blood and spreads to the skin. That is what turns the skin yellow. The immune cells see the bilirubin and release histamine (like an allergic reaction). It is like having poison ivy all over your body but it is inside your skin. One day I squatted down in the kitchen to get a pot and couldn't stand back up. No matter how hard I tried, I just couldn't get back up. I had to crawl into the living room and pull myself up onto the couch. I had never experienced anything like this before. There was no hiding how sick I still was, or how much healing I had left to do. There would be no "pushing through" this. I had to walk through every bit of it.

A few months passed, and as I was trying to do everything I could to get better, my low-grade fevers started to come back. Before my liver shut down, I'd get these fevers in the evening. Not a true fever in the medical world, but that temperature of around 99.8°F. I was so tired. I called Dr. Jophlin, who wanted me to get a CT scan right away. I could tell she was concerned and so was I. Things were stable, but I was going to need to get blood work and wait for the results.

The second big blow almost took me out. I got a call from a good friend of mine who said, "Karla, I don't know how to tell you this, but there was a group of women at a restaurant talking specifics about your liver. You think these women are your friends, but they aren't." A wave of nauseating panic ran through me. The weight was just too heavy. I was sobbing on my bed crying out to God, *Please help me, please take the pain away. I don't know how to get through this.* I had always numbed feelings like this. That's when I remember getting a message loud and clear: *You need to lean on me. That's what I've been wanting you to do the whole time.* It shook me to my core. It was so true. During all the years I had struggled, I ultimately went to wine for comfort. I pushed my way through things. This journey needed to be different.

CHAPTER 8

BACK TO DARKNESS, MY OLD FRIEND

This chapter is hard to write. It's hard to write because what I did is truly insane. I mentioned earlier that my experience of getting sick again would teach me about friendships and the power of the subconscious brain. Unfortunately, it wasn't until years afterward that I really learned about the power of the subconscious and why the following happened. Now this is something I can teach others about in my coaching to help stop them from stepping back onto that slippery slope, or at least help them from sliding all the way back to the bottom and staying there, like I did.

I drank again.

It was a while after my fevers started coming back and I got that infamous CT scan. My doctor ran a lot of bloodwork and discovered that I had good ol' mono. Typically, the Epstein-Barr virus causes mononucleosis. Looking back, though, I see the power in something called confirmation bias: the search for information that will confirm a belief. In my case, I wanted desperately to believe that Epstein-Barr caused my mono and mono caused my liver to shut down. I didn't want to believe that my drinking was the cause of it all. So, I Googled myself an answer confirming that it was mono that caused my liver's demise, not my precious alcohol. When "Dr. Google" showed me that mono can impact the liver and cause temporary jaundice, it was all my brain needed to convince me that I didn't actually have a drinking problem. Of course, I confirmed all of this inside my own head and not with my physician.

I've since learned that the Epstein-Barr virus can significantly affect the liver in many ways and could've had a hand in catapulting me into liver failure. In no way should this take away from the fact that my drinking was the real culprit, but at the time, I was grasping at straws. I wanted to believe that I could moderate my drinking and be "normal." After all, drinking was fun, and it was the one thing that helped me relax. I tried so hard. I desperately wanted to numb the pain from the gossip. *Alcohol is the only thing that would help* was the lie I kept telling myself.

I began romanticizing what it would be like to drink again one day. A tiny thought grew into an itch that needed to be scratched. It grew until I finally made the decision that I'd just try a glass of wine. Alone, of course, because somewhere inside, I knew I shouldn't be doing it. It's those darn subconscious beliefs; they win 100 percent of the time until we address them. Willpower is finite and only lasts a certain amount of time, and my white-knuckling time was up. I remember sipping on the glass of wine while desperately wanting to think that this wouldn't be a problem. At the time, I knew nothing about neural pathways and why my attempt at "controlled drinking" wouldn't work. I just knew alcohol helped me. So without knowing it, I stepped onto one of the slipperiest slopes I've ever been on: the cycle of waking up every morning promising myself that I wouldn't drink again that night. How in the world did I get here again?

This time I truly felt stuck because I didn't know how to admit to anyone the mistake I'd made. My old "Little Miss Fix It" self was back and as ineffective as ever. This went on for months.

A lot happened in that time. The biggest is that I got married. Yes, that's right. After everything that happened to me, Grady proposed. This sweet, selfless man saw through all of that ick and loved me anyway. I only wish this had been enough to show me that I could tell him anything and he'd be there. Instead, I thought being honest with him would only make him change his mind about me. So I just tried to fix it. (Yes, I know. The definition of insanity.)

I also began working again and went right back to picking up those plates and trying to spin them. I knew this couldn't last for long—and it didn't.

I truly believe God puts certain people in our path for a reason. God also gives us free will, so it's up to us what we want to act on. As a physician liaison, I met new physicians who were entering the hospital system. This is when I met one of the other key physicians who became my rock during another difficult time in my life, Dr. Allen. She was a mixture of sweet and smart and had a clear streak of badass in her. I knew she'd know what to do, it was just a matter of my shame unchoking me long enough to let me get the words out.

One morning, I noticed what looked like broken blood vessels all over my chest and went straight to the mirror to check my eyes. Yellow. I don't know how long I cried on the bathroom floor, but the cold tiles seemed to be the only thing that helped cool the rage inside me. I was so angry with myself. How could I do this? How could I do this to Grady? Here was a man who loved me no matter what, and I turned to an old liquid friend that never brought me anything but pain.

I'd been in toxic relationships before but never thought about the parallels to my relationship with alcohol. It's similar to when you break up with someone and, after some time goes by, you start thinking about the good times you had together. Your ex sends a text, and it brings back that warm, fuzzy feeling inside. All the abuse, name calling, and cheating is dulled, and you begin thinking, *Was it really that bad? We had some good times, right?* It's called the fading affect bias, commonly referred to as FAB. It's a psychological phenomenon in which memories associated with negative emotions are forgotten about more quickly than those attached to positive emotions. Researchers have studied the phenomenon for decades, and I'm sure you can think of times when you experienced FAB in your life. It's not until you decide to give it another go that everything comes crashing back and you vividly remember why you broke up in the first place.

As soon as I started to slide down that slippery slope, I remembered why I had broken up with alcohol. One of the most dangerous things about alcohol is that it makes our bodies truly believe we need it. I thought I needed it. In turn, it was killing me.

After my ugly cry on the bathroom floor, I called my sweet Grady and told him what I had done. He came home and I ugly cried again. He held me and told me it was going to be okay, even though I know that at that time he didn't think it would be. Would this be our life? Me stopping and starting to drink again? We didn't yet know that this day, September 9th, 2014, would be the last day I would drink. Still, I had a huge uphill battle to climb. Those red spots on my chest were spider hemangioma, which was a sign that my liver was shutting down. Again.

<hr>

I sat in Dr. Allen's parking lot for a long time. "Mrs. Fix It" tried to step in and prevent me from speaking honestly. My shame about what I had done was like a huge weight holding me in place. I was naive at the time about what was really happening, and I'm glad I was. I thought I'd just let her know about my slip up, she'd put me on steroids again to get things back on track, and I'd be good to go. Unfortunately, my assumptions and answers from "Dr. Google" were incorrect.

Dr. Allen took one look at me and knew I wasn't well. She got the ball rolling on bloodwork and the results were awful. When she called to explain that I needed to go back to the hospital in Charleston, I sobbed. I begged and pleaded to stay home. My temper tantrum didn't work, and back to Charleston Grady and I went.

I didn't know this at the time, but Grady was mentally preparing for me not to be around anymore. He knew what the numbers meant and what was happening. Years after this event, he told me that he would look at me and know there was a possibility that I wasn't going to be around for the next season of our favorite show or the next fall to watch the Clemson Tigers play. He worried he'd be a widower after less than a year of marriage. He never let on to me that he felt this way, or how bad things were. My stoic, loving husband sat by my bedside, continued to believe in me, and prayed that he was wrong.

One day, I was lying in my bed in the hospital, alone and quite honestly wallowing in my sorrow. It was heavy and dark. There was a knock at the door, and in walked Dr. Jophlin. I was so happy to see her, but I quickly remembered that I had failed her. She had believed in me. She *saw* me, while others made assumptions. And yet I just went back to drinking like all the others. I couldn't even look at her. Dr. Allen had called her to let her know what happened and that I was back in the hospital. Dr. Jophlin took the time to find me and come visit me, and she even brought a little plant from the gift shop. We then had a conversation that would change the direction of my life. She sat with me and told me part of her personal journey and why she became a hepatologist. She had seen the destruction that alcohol caused so many people during her college years and how easily it could've done the same to her. She said to me, "Karla, you aren't less than anybody else. You aren't different. I see the destruction that alcohol causes, so I see it as a positive. It's not that you *can't* drink anymore … You don't *have* to drink anymore. Give yourself that gift. I gave myself that gift a long time ago."

In that moment, there was a huge shift in me. Dr. Jophlin opened this beautiful space of grace that allowed me to put my boxing gloves down long enough to hear her. It reignited a spark in me. Light pushes out darkness.

There was so much power in the words "don't have to" versus "can't." There was so much strength in this young, smart, professional, beautiful young woman sharing a piece of her story to help me with mine. I knew right then that I wanted to give someone else the gift she had given me. I had no idea what that would look like, but I knew I was going to fight to live. And I didn't have to drink anymore to do it.

SECTION 2
HEALING ON MY OWN TERMS

CHAPTER 9

BUBBLE BATHS & POPSICLE STICKS

I was out of the hospital, but there was so much healing that needed to happen. I still felt so weak and sick, and I sure looked unhealthy. My coloring had moved from Oompa Loompa orange to pale gray. I couldn't believe how much my muscles had atrophied during my time at the hospital. Nighttime was the worst. Fear would set in, and the "what ifs" would start having a party in my head. *What if I die tonight?* was the thought that stood out above the rest. I wanted Connie at my bedside so bad. What I wouldn't give for one of her hugs.

My GI system was totally out of whack, and so was my bloodwork. I'd wake up to find my pillow soaked in blood from a nosebleed I had in the middle of the night. During the day I could just be standing there one minute, and the next minute a huge clot of blood would come pouring out of my nose. It was so scary. My hair was falling out in big clumps, and I thought for sure if I washed my hair too many times I wouldn't have any left at all. Sadly, I remember celebrating when I could go to the bathroom and see that my urine was a healthy yellow again instead of a sickly brown. I had never before imagined celebrating such a thing.

My body had been beaten up and broken, and only time would tell if it was going to heal itself. I was determined to do whatever was in my control to help it along the way. This was such a crucial time in my journey. That spark deep inside was determined to burn hot enough to heal me, and I knew I was going to need to kindle it in my own way. I needed to learn from my mistakes—learn from what had worked for me so far and what hadn't. The world was telling me to go one direction, but that fire in me was telling me a different story.

If I wanted to move forward, I needed to learn how and why I had gotten to where I was. I had this visual that I was a cross between a private investigator and an attorney who was representing myself on a crucial case. My hands needed to be free of the cuffs that had kept me restrained for so long. This case was important because my life depended on it.

As I started to get visibly healthier, my fear of what it was going to be like to live forever in this new way started to grow. Could I really do this? What kept me going was a fire in my belly that told me there was so much more to this, and that life didn't have to be a one-day-at-a-time struggle.

I felt like I was sitting in the driver's seat of a new car, about to go on a journey, and I wasn't quite sure where I was going. I didn't have a physical map, but I was going to count on my internal GPS. I hadn't paid attention to that GPS in a while, so everything felt foreign and uncomfortable. I needed to learn the ins and outs of this new car.

I'm an introvert at heart, so sitting back and becoming an observer wasn't hard for me. Socially, I wasn't going out at all, and for me that was a very important first step. It wasn't like I went out and partied all the time. I drank at home. I needed my home to become a safe space where I could process all of this and figure out my next steps.

I was sitting on my couch one day and saw something that triggered a painful, panicky feeling in me. I said aloud, "Wow, so this is what it's like to feel." Before, I hadn't allowed those painful emotions to sit with me for long without numbing them. So this time, instead of reaching for alcohol, I went straight for the tub, grabbing a popsicle out of the freezer on the way. There was something about the combination of a warm bath and a cold popsicle that did the trick, so the practice became one of my go-to habits whenever I'd start becoming overwhelmed. You could tell how hard of a time I was having by the number of popsicle sticks on the side of the tub. I can't tell you how many bubble baths and popsicles I had those first few months, but I know our local Publix was having to restock Outshine bars like crazy.

What I didn't realize at the time was that I was creating a new healthy outlet for myself. Yes, I realize that popsicles aren't exactly healthy, but I was learning that things other than alcohol could help calm me when I started feeling stressed or anxious. Another remedy was reading books at night. I hadn't read like that in years. It used to be that I'd drink my wine until I was ready to pass out, so there was no room for reading. I even tried old-school crossword puzzles, the kind you buy when you're checking out at the grocery store. I preferred the ones that had the word EASY in all caps across the front. I wasn't looking to challenge myself at night, I was just trying to disconnect and quiet my brain. And it worked.

The contributing factor to why these novel tools worked was that I had a new sense of calm. I don't want to say I was anxiety-free, because I wasn't. But there was something different after I had been alcohol-free for a month or so. It was as though my internal engine had shifted gears; I wasn't so revved up. This was a sensation I was honestly shocked by. When I was drinking, one of my biggest concerns had been what to do with my anxiety. I truly believed that alcohol was the ONLY thing that helped me. Where did my intense anxiety go? I was determined to find out. But in the meantime, I was going to hang onto this unfamiliar yet gratifying sense of calm. I had this protectiveness over it, like it was a precious new gift I had been given, and I'd be damned if someone was going to take it away from me. Here's the simple truth: If alcohol had *really* helped me with anxiety, I would've been the least anxious person ever. Things that make you go *hmmmmm* …

CHAPTER 10

DINNERS, PARTIES, AND BOOK CLUBS, OH MY

It sounds dramatic to say that socializing felt like stepping into a new world, but when I think about it, I had used alcohol to help me socialize since I was in college. By the time I was 37 years old, alcohol had been my sidekick for almost 20 years. TWENTY YEARS! My social anxiety was very real, and I now see that my urges to drink were because of that anxiety and not because the wine paired well with the shrimp. I drank because I thought it helped me relax. I thought it made me a better version of myself. It calmed down all the automatic negative thoughts (ANTs)[1] that were typically crawling all over me when I went out with people. *I always wear this outfit, it's the only thing that fits. They think I'm boring. I don't ever have anything to offer to the conversation. What if I have a panic attack in there; everyone will think I'm crazy. What if people see my hands shaking …* The list went on and on. So I drank to quiet the voices. What would going out be like without my crutch? It was all so new to me.

One of the hardest things about socializing was that I didn't know what to tell people about why I wasn't drinking. I was so insecure about what people would think. I had a lot of new people that I saw socially, as being married and becoming a mom brought with it a lot of them. The new people I was around may or may not have even known I'd been sick, let alone that alcohol had catapulted me into a hospital bed.

I remember being so nervous going out with another couple for the first time after my recovery. What was I going to say? I told Grady beforehand that he needed to order a beer or a cocktail because I didn't want people thinking we weren't fun or that we were judging them for their drinking. Looking back, I see I was a wreck. All my Southern husband wanted was a sweet tea with his dinner, and here I was forcing him to drink so we could look "normal." I later found

---

[1] Dr. Daniel Gregory Amen, "ANT Therapy," American Holistic Health Association, accessed November 16, 2021, https://ahha.org/selfhelp-articles/ant-therapy/.

out that the people we went out with thought for sure I wasn't drinking because I must be pregnant.

Going to my first book club was an interesting experience as well. I was still trying to get better at making some new friends and being at least a little social, so when someone I just met invited me to a book club, I said yes. I was so proud of myself. I showed up at a stranger's house with a book in hand, ready to discuss the chapters I'd read. The host cordially offered me a glass of wine. I politely declined and asked if she had any water. She said, "Yes, but are you sure you don't want some wine? I have white, red, and we have all kinds of options for cocktails too." I politely declined. Again. I felt so awkward and out of place.

We didn't discuss the book that evening; it was just a group of women getting out of the house to drink. I remember being so glad I drove my own car because all I wanted was to go home. I couldn't help but wonder what it would be like if the reverse happened. What if you went to a party, the hostess asked you if you would like anything to drink, you asked for a glass of wine, and in return they said, "Yes, we have wine, but are you sure you don't want a glass of water or herbal tea instead?" I'm telling you right now, that would go over like a lead balloon. People would be so offended.

Socializing made me face a few things that I really hadn't anticipated. First, I thought I'd look at other people drinking and crave what they had, but that didn't happen. I was so overwhelmed with what to say or not say that I didn't feel comfortable in my own skin. Second, I couldn't help but recognize the hypocrisy in our society when it comes to alcohol. It's so clear that people blame the drinker, but they seldom examine what's in the bottle and blame the drink. People are so protective of that precious liquid.

CHAPTER 11

WHY ME?

"Pity party" is what comes to mind when I think about a stage that I went through about three to four months into not drinking.

In the beginning, I physically felt so much better. I constantly saw physical improvements such as better sleep, healthier skin, and brighter eyes. There are so many benefits that come with not drinking. Still, I couldn't help but think, *Why me? What's wrong with me?* I actually said to my parents, "Yeah, thanks for all the wacky genes you passed along. I get the tremors and issues with alcohol. Lovely. [Insert lots of sarcasm]." Whew! Talk about feeling bad for myself.

Why me? Why did I get stuck while others didn't? Bitterness rose in me and it felt horrible. I knew of other people who drank a lot, and they didn't end up in the hospital. So why and how did I get so stuck? There was a passion in me to figure this out. I needed the answers so I could move on and not be so angry.

I had heard before that drinking for medicinal purposes was not a good thing. When I heard that, I thought "medicinal" only referred to things like physical pain. Recently, I heard someone explain drinking for medicinal reasons in a way that made total sense to me—the three M's. At first, alcohol seems like a MIRACLE; it works like a charm. For example, alcohol might initially work great for checking out at the end of a hard day. But eventually that leads to MEDICINAL use because you're using it whenever you feel stressed about something. It becomes the medicine you take to calm down. Unfortunately, this leads to absolute MISERY.

So if alcohol was such a good fix initially, how does it end in misery? Well, our amazing bodies immediately recognize that a toxin has entered our system and work diligently to remove it. The more consistently we drink, the better our bodies get at breaking it down and clearing it out. This increases our tolerance, so we need more of that substance to get the same effect that we had before. I vividly recall this happening to me. I remember walking out of my room on so many mornings and seeing the wine bottle from the night before. I had promised myself that I would only have a glass or two of wine, but by the look of the bottle, I clearly had much more than that. Over time, a small bottle became a big bottle, and I drank more and more without getting the effect I was looking for. This process didn't happen overnight; it took time. But the shame of seeing that bottle the next day started taking over and I didn't want to see it anymore. So I hid it.

Instead of saying that I used alcohol for medicinal purposes, I explain it this way: I started off by giving alcohol a job. Its job was to help me with anxiety at social events. Then I started promoting it and giving it more responsibilities, and it just started weaving its way into my world. I didn't want it to. I was scared. But life keeps going no matter what we're going through. Stressful days at work don't stop because we want to stop drinking. And when we try to step away, we realize our feet won't move and we're stuck. We get caught in our own roots.

CHAPTER 12

ROOTS

Why me? is a question that comes up for many people. Why does one person struggle with alcohol more than someone else? This is where people love to bring up the topic of genetics. This is also the mindset that creates the line in the sand of "us versus them." It's the "They can do it and I can't … We're cut from a different cloth" mindset—a mindset that's incorrect and can be dangerous. Many people think that they can't be an alcoholic because it doesn't run in their family. The bottom line is that alcohol is addictive to humans. Period. Alcohol is a carcinogenic, addictive substance that doesn't care who your mom and dad are, how much money you have, or what color your skin is. Alcohol is just what it is and never changes. Here is the uncomplicated truth: while genes can contribute to your risk of becoming addicted to alcohol, environmental and social factors weigh heavily as well. So genetics play a role, but hear me loud and clear on this: there is no specific gene for alcoholism.

I tell people that alcohol wore many hats in my life. As I mentioned, I gave it many jobs. The "jobs" I gave it look like roots. The roots are tied up in our beliefs about how alcohol serves us. The problem is, by the time we realize that alcohol isn't serving us the way we think it is, some of those roots have grown too deep and we're already stuck. The beautiful thing is, we aren't stuck forever. It takes some digging to find freedom from our roots. Sometimes we think we're free, but we soon realize that we didn't remove the entire root and our subconscious still thinks the root serves us somehow. That doesn't mean we're doomed. It just means we have more digging to do to get the whole thing out.

Some roots are easier to pull up than others. Sometimes those roots are deep. I think about pulling weeds here in South Carolina, and there's some that are just so nasty you'd better have gloves on when trying to pull them up. Some roots are not only strong and deeply rooted but also have thorns that can prick you on the way up. It can be painful, but once they're pulled, it's very satisfying.

ROOTS 67

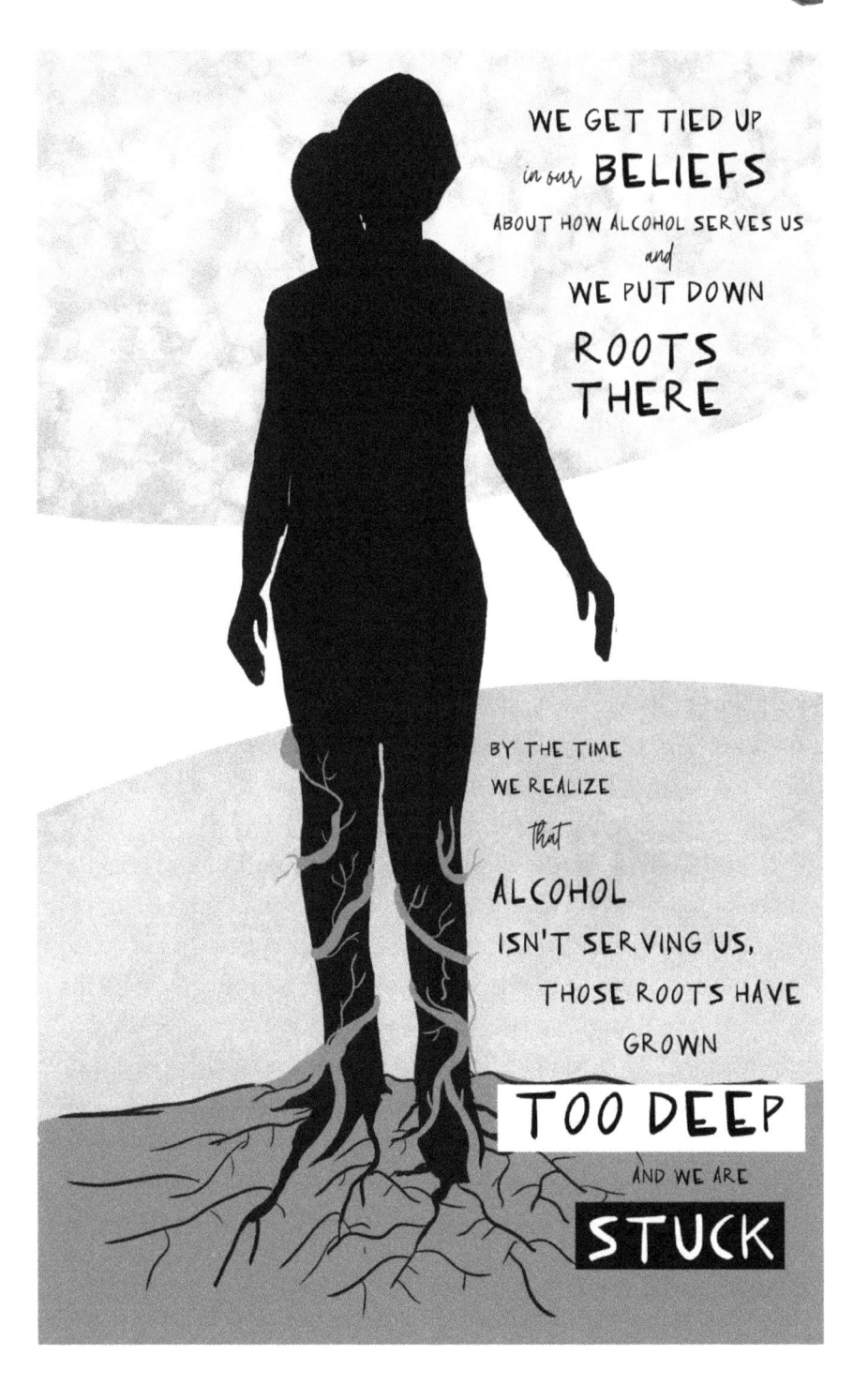

WE GET TIED UP *in our* BELIEFS ABOUT HOW ALCOHOL SERVES US *and* WE PUT DOWN ROOTS THERE

BY THE TIME WE REALIZE *that* ALCOHOL ISN'T SERVING US, THOSE ROOTS HAVE GROWN TOO DEEP AND WE ARE STUCK

This is a great picture of what it's like to work through some different beliefs around alcohol. The beliefs we have are the roots we struggle to remove.

Some beliefs about alcohol focus on the substance itself. For example, I had a client who honestly believed alcohol helped him sleep. Let's tackle this with science. It's widely known in the medical world that alcohol negatively affects sleep. Even one drink disrupts sleep patterns. While this is common knowledge in the medical world, it's not very common in the general public. Remember, our beliefs form from our experiences and what we learn from our environment. Alcohol can temporarily relieve tension and that feeling of exhaustion from a rough day. Unfortunately, most people don't realize how temporary that is; it doesn't even last a whole night. When someone goes to sleep without alcohol in their system, they go through two altering states of sleep: slow wave sleep (SWS) and rapid eye movement (REM) sleep. SWS is just like it sounds—deep, restful sleep. REM sleep is less restful and is usually associated with dreaming. REM sleep is just as essential to our health as SWS. In tests with rats, lack of REM sleep led to death in just a matter of weeks.[2] Alcohol, even just one drink, interrupts both REM sleep and SWS.

In addition, our bodies produce natural chemicals and hormones that help us sleep. When we drink on a regular basis, our bodies cease to produce them. The brain recognizes a depressant on board, so it stops telling the body to release the natural sleep hormones. This is another reason people struggle so much with sleep when they first stop drinking. Their bodies have become so used to alcohol being in the picture that they stop doing what they do naturally.

Understanding the chemical effects of alcohol on sleep is just the beginning. A second powerful step in the process of pulling up the root is experience. People can read about the science of it all day long,

---

[2] Everson CA, Bergmann BM, Rechtschaffen A. Sleep deprivation in rat:II. Total sleep deprivation. Sleep. 1989 Feb;12(1):13–21. doi:10.1093/sleep/12.1.13. PMID: 2928622.

ROOTS 69

Alcohol & The Sleep Cycle

Alcohol may help you "pass out" but it negatively impacts the quality of your sleep.

HEALTHY SLEEP CYCLE

SLEEP CYCLE AFTER DRINKING

FALL ASLEEP

REPEATS 2-3 TIMES EACH NIGHT
*VARIES BY INDIVIDUAL

DRIFTING OFF

UNCONSCIOUS

PASSING OUT

Slow Wave Sleep (SWS)

THE "3AM WAKE-UP"

Rapid Eye Movement Sleep (REM)- associated with dreaming.

OR NOT..

"SNORE"

REFRESHED

EXHAUSTED

Alcohol, even just one drink, interrupts both REM sleep and SWS, leaving you exhausted over time, even if you "slept" all night.

WAKE UP

but they need to experience the negative effects of alcohol on sleep to truly debunk the subconscious belief that alcohol is serving them in some way. I've seen devices that help people track their sleep, the results of which can be very impactful. When people compare their sleep patterns during the time they were drinking with their sleep patterns after they stopped drinking, they see jaw-dropping results. Science plus experience can be such a beautiful thing.

An example of a root that goes a little bit deeper is the belief about alcohol and socializing. Drinking alcohol while socializing is extremely common in many societies, and alcohol has crept its way into pretty much every gathering we can think of. From kids' birthday parties to gatherings with friends, alcohol is not only welcome but often expected—even at baby showers, an event centered around someone who shouldn't drink for the health of their growing baby. The mindset of many people is that if an event serves alcohol, more people will come. And these people aren't even those high-priced marketing gurus employed by the alcohol industry; they are everyday individuals who are just trying to get people to come to an event. I've seen it done everywhere from churches to the medical community. "Have cocktails at the Easter egg hunt; more people will come." "Let's have an event with mimosas and mammograms to get the people to come." Disappointingly, it's most recently been, "Hey, let's offer free beer and get people to come get a vaccine." Do we not see a glaring problem here? It's staring us right in the face. But people want to protect and defend that substance to the very end. It makes me sad.

When people first stop drinking, social events can be very difficult to attend. This is another deep root and another place where I see the "us versus them" concept be so hurtful and painfully inaccurate. Because alcohol sits so high on a pedestal, people assume everyone drinks except for pregnant women and "people with problems." This was one of the things that so glaringly stood out to me once I started my own health journey. It makes people uncomfortable when you don't drink. I've even heard the phrase, "I don't trust people who don't drink." This root is more difficult to pull free. However, with time and practice, it's not only doable but can also become your new norm. And, oh, is that a beautiful place to be.

This next root, I'll be honest, is a real bitch. I equate it to this weed I've encountered in my yard many times. It creeps along the ground looking innocent until you try to pull that bad boy up, and then it can become really painful. This is the level of self. In my life, alcohol wore many hats at this level. I thought it made me a normal person—a better person. I thought it was what made me confident and "fixed" me. I thought it made me worthy. But believing these things is what kept me stuck. These roots pulled me so hard that they almost took me completely under.

Pulling our roots is an arduous process. It's part of the reason so many people fail when they try to stop drinking. Saying you're powerless against alcohol and trying to make it one day at a time only lasts so long. You have to address the deeper layers in order to find your true freedom. It can take some time, but those roots will pull free. I honestly don't think you can truly work on these deeper issues until you remove alcohol. And removing alcohol is just the first step in healing. You may need to seek help from a specialist who can walk you through your trauma wounds. Regardless, you have to stop trying to put a Band-Aid on them and ignoring them. Neglecting your wounds will only make you sicker.

CHAPTER 13

MY WALK OF SHAME

Shame is a hefty topic. One of my goals is to one day sit down and talk with Brené Brown, a professor, lecturer, and author who is known in particular for her research on shame,. You know, just have a casual chat over tea about how this one word carries so much weight and can keep people anchored to pain and unhappiness for years. It's something some people never find freedom from.

Shame is a word I used a lot in the past. To be honest, I'm only now coming to terms with just how much it impacted me, both before and after I started my alcohol-free health journey. I know I'm not alone in this. Many people talk about shame without really educating themselves about it, and most people talk about it without wanting to open and look into their own dark closets.

According to Oxford University Press, shame is "the painful feeling of humiliation or distress caused by the consciousness of wrong or foolish behavior."[3] Just from this definition we can see how shame is all kinds of wrapped up in drinking alcohol.

We all have a belief story about alcohol that is based on things people tell us as we grow up and the things we see and experience. Our culture is constantly feeding into our belief stories with ads from the alcohol industry. So many people think they aren't affected by commercials or ads. Years ago, I was one of those people. Unfortunately, those who believe that are wrong. There is big money in the alcohol business, and I promise you the industry knows the ads work or they wouldn't spend billions of dollars a year on them. The ads tap into our basic human desire for love and belonging. Do yourself a favor and start paying attention to the ads you see. What are they telling you? They're selling fun, sex, togetherness, etc., all with the intent to influence your belief story.

My belief story was that alcohol was a normal and exciting thing you got to do at a certain age. It was something that family did when

---

[3] Oxford University Press, s.v. "Shame," Lexico.com, accessed November 17, 2021, https://www.lexico.com/ene/definition/shame.

they came together, something that created fun. I remember often hearing that people who drink alone have a problem with alcohol and might be alcoholics. Well, I lived alone in my 20s, so I surely drank alone. I joked with people that since I talked on the phone while I drank my wine I wasn't really alone, right? But deep down I wondered if it was wrong.

My walk of shame included doing things I wouldn't normally do if I wasn't under the influence. I thought alcohol made me bolder, but all it did was make me feel small. Drinking didn't look like those sexy commercials I saw; it looked like regret and pain. On the day I tried to tell my physician that I was struggling, shame is what kept me quiet. Shame was my ultimate mute button. Shame told me, "Don't talk about that because then everyone will know you are different." I remember hearing people talk about others and their out-of-control drinking, and how I'd curiously join in the conversation. One time, I said that I felt bad for the person who was slurring their words because I had done that, too. What I heard back was, "Yeah, well, you're not an alcoholic so you don't have to worry about that." Inside I was screaming, *I'm scared! I'm struggling! I don't know what to do!* But I hit my mute button. More shame.

Another shameful topic that's painful for a lot of people to discuss is drinking and driving. Talk about foolish, wrong behavior that you consciously know is wrong! It's a whopper of one. I still think about the times that I drove when I shouldn't have, and all I can do is thank God nothing happened. It feels horrible to write about, but it's the truth. It's one of the hardest things for my clients to talk about, and there's a reason for that: We know better, but we do it anyway.

We also feel shame when we feel labeled. I remember talking to a physician after I had gotten healthy. I was getting a little bolder in sharing what happened to me ("a little" being the key words here). When I discussed that I had gone into acute liver failure, the physician's response was, "Well, you don't have cirrhosis, do you?" Coupled with the look on their face, those words had me wanting to crawl into a hole. As I'll talk about later in the book, fighting for my life in the hospital *had* left me with the "battle wound" of cirrhosis. I responded by saying, "Oh, thank goodness, no I don't." Oh, the shame.

A client I recently worked with had a similar experience. She suddenly became sick and developed ascites. When she was at the doctor's office, staff assured her that she couldn't have cirrhosis because "you'd have to be drinking daily for years" to get something like that. In her head, she knew that she checked off that box, but shame kept her mute button pressed. This client is a young, beautiful, professional woman with two small kids. She doesn't match up with the world's view of who would have cirrhosis. Even if she didn't have it, the problem was that their words strongly impacted her shame. She didn't feel free to discuss her truth because she was ashamed and afraid of what they might think about her. I know this feeling all too well.

The crazy thing about shame is that it can't survive when you bring it into the light. When you keep shame in a dark closet, it builds a foundation and grows. But in light, it shrivels away. When I started my coaching business years ago, I was truly holding onto two different worlds. My personal life was a world in which I was a woman who just didn't drink and didn't talk about drinking. The other, my coaching business, was a world in which I felt safe to talk about my story and not be ashamed of it. The longer I traveled on my health journey, the more passionate I became about telling my side of the story. It became increasingly difficult to hold onto both worlds. I was terrified. What I see clearly now is that shame was holding me back. It was like an anchor fixed tightly to the bottom of the sea. My shame only let me move so far before pulling me back. It was stopping me from finding freedom.

I'll never forget when I learned the power of shining a light on shame. It was after pulling the trigger and starting my business by making it "Facebook official." That's a big deal these days. As soon as

I pulled that trigger, so many ANTs began crawling all over me. *What will people say? What will they think? What if I regret this?* I knew that once I put it out there, I wasn't going to be able to take it back. At the time, my daughter was taking dance lessons. At first, I worried about how awkward it was going to be to sit in a small hallway full of parents waiting for their girls to finish their "Twirling for Twos" class. But when I walked into that hallway, I never felt so confident. It didn't matter to me that most of the people there had no idea that I had hit the "post" button on my website and first blog. There was a sense of freedom inside me that I hadn't felt before. A weight had been lifted.

As I've continued sharing my story, I've held onto that feeling of freedom. I've had to hold onto it tight while writing this book. The fear is heavy and can be distracting. But I just keep going back to the day I walked into that dance hall. The lightness in my chest made me feel like I could finally take a breath and relax. And if that's what happened over a business and a blog, I can only imagine the healing that will happen inside me when I open all my dark closets and let the contents spill out onto these pages. The best part, the part that makes it all worth it, is knowing that in doing so, I will be helping someone else out there.

CHAPTER 14

MY NAME IS KARLA
AND I'M NOT AN ALCOHOLIC

I started calling this my health journey from the very beginning. It felt right to me. I wanted to do everything I could to improve my health. I wanted to eat right, exercise, all the things. I wanted to LIVE, damn it.

When I left the hospital, I was given a list of resources consisting of different AA meetings and Celebrate Recovery meetings. I had been to these types of meetings before. Many, actually. Over the years of worrying that I was drinking too much, I'd go check them out because I thought doing so was the only way people could stop drinking. It's not. Not even close. I actually walked away from these meetings saying, "I don't really have a problem." People kept telling me to take one day at a time, and all I could think was, *So you mean every day is going to be hard to get through without alcohol? Am I going to think about alcohol every day and wish I had it?* Dang, that sounded depressing.

One of my main sticking points with these meetings is that I never have and never will label myself as an alcoholic. This is when I usually get the head tilt from people who think, "Aww, bless her heart. She's just not admitting what she is yet." Honestly, it's not that I'm being stubborn or refusing to accept something about myself; it's that The 12 Steps didn't jive with my life experience. At the beginning of 12-step meetings, you go around the room and introduce yourself, and then you label yourself. It's part of the process. Saying, "Hi, I'm Karla, and I'm an alcoholic" made me cringe. Not only that, but I also felt so detached from the label that when I said it I felt like I was lying to the group.

Most of the time when I talk about this, people think I want to leave the door open to drink again or don't want to admit the problem that I had with alcohol. But it wasn't about that. Saying that I had a disease and was powerless didn't feel right. And there was supposed to be this huge divide between us ("alcoholics") and them ("normal drinkers"). About a year before I got sick, I had a conversation with someone who didn't know about my internal battle with

MY NAME IS KARLA AND I'M NOT AN ALCOHOLIC

OUTDATED THINKING about ALCOHOL ADDICTION DIVIDES PEOPLE into 2 FALSE CATEGORIES

"NORMAL" — OR — **"ALCOHOLIC"**

PLEASE ANYTHING HELP

The reality is that Alcohol Use Disorder (AUD) occurs across a spectrum with categories like MILD, MODERATE and SEVERE. It can be difficult to determine where any individual is on the spectrum based on their appearance.

THE SPECTRUM of ALCOHOL USE DISORDER (AUD)

SEVERE — WORRIED BUT SAYING NOTHING — RELYING ON for STRESS RELIEF — GIVING alcohol A JOB — NEEDING IT to SOCIALIZE — BREAKING YOUR OWN RULES — MODERATE — USING to SLEEP — CHEMICALLY DEPENDENT — MILD

The term "alcoholic" is also problematic because it makes the disorder about the PERSON, not about the SUBSTANCE. The Diagnostic and Statistical Manual of Mental Disorders no longer uses this term.

alcohol. They were talking about their 12-step meetings and said, "You wouldn't understand [about alcohol]. You and I aren't cut from the same cloth. We [alcoholics] are different from other people." That mindset is a dangerous one. This "us versus them" mentality is widely accepted in our society and it's just not correct. But more about that later …

Our society has also taken on the belief that the 12-step way is the only way to successfully stop drinking. People walk around with this sense of being in a safe, protective bubble because alcoholism doesn't run in their family. Far too many Dr. Phil shows on the topic have led the public to think they are experts as well. After watching a few of them, I'd seriously love to know the last time the good ol' Doc himself brushed up on this topic. In one episode, he insisted that a guest admit out loud to the world that they were an alcoholic. "Say it!" Dr. Phil demanded. Finally, the guest relented and said it. So what just happened there, McGraw? You pressured someone to label himself. Did that fix him? No, you actually just shamed a person into submission. I wonder what that person's tool is for dealing with that emotion?

The term *alcoholic* is actually an outdated one. The Diagnostic and Statistical Manual of Mental Disorders, which is what the medical community uses as a standard to diagnose and treat patients, doesn't use this term anymore. Instead, the publication uses the term *alcohol use disorder* with the classifications mild, moderate, and severe.

I ended up feeling somewhat rejected from the recovery community. I honestly didn't fit in. The world was telling me I was doing this recovery thing wrong, and I felt very alone.

A little later in my health journey, I saw an advertisement for a recovery coaching certification happening right up the road from me. In looking up the details, I saw that recovery coaching was accepting of ALL paths to people finding freedom. Had I finally found my people? I went to the first day of the certification and quickly realized that I wasn't going to fit in there, either. Instructors taught that to not identify as an "alcoholic" was shameful. Every part of me disagreed. One day, a woman who I know and admire because she is kind and would give the shirt off her back to help other people, raised her hand and said, referring to me, "I just don't understand how she is going to help anyone when she's never even been to jail." Wait, what? We were able to talk this out reasonably, but that statement alone shows there is a huge gap of awareness about who is struggling with alcohol. We have to stop painting the picture of people with alcohol use disorder being the ones who get DUIs, go to jail, lose their jobs, and stumble around drunk, and open our eyes to who people with alcohol use disorder really are. People struggling with alcohol look like the soccer mom at the field holding a Yeti cup filled with her drink of choice. They look like the mom in her minivan headed to yoga with a massive hangover. They look like a young man in a fraternity just doing "what boys do in college." They look like a healthcare provider having a drink early in the morning so they can sleep after working the night shift.

We also need to stop thinking there is only one way to change.

Dr. Barry Duncan wrote a book called *What's Right with You: Debunking Dysfunction and Changing Your Life*. There are so many great nuggets in this book; I highly recommend it. Dr. Duncan addresses the fact that society seems to disregard an individual's theory of change. This is exactly what happened to me. I strongly believed that going the AA route just didn't fit me and my journey, and people repeatedly told me I was wrong. Dr. Duncan states, "Disregarding an individual's theory of change explains why many attempts at change fail and why many therapies are unsuccessful."[4] He and his colleagues found that even the most "impossible cases" could find success when their own ideas were recruited and

---

[4] Barry L. Duncan, *What's Right with You: Debunking Dysfunction and Changing Your Life* (Florida: Health Communications, Inc., 2005), # 87–89.

implemented. Other studies out there back this up when it comes to the treatment of alcohol dependency.

Not identifying as an alcoholic and not going to meetings didn't mean that I was denying my issue. It was actually me standing up for myself for the first time in a long time. I wasn't going to submit to something that made no sense to me. Why? Because I desperately wanted this journey to be a successful one. Denying how I felt inside would've set me up for failure. I was going to ignore the people blessing my heart and expecting me to fail. And I was going to set out to find other people like me out there in the world, because I knew I couldn't be alone. I needed to find my people. And I did.

Before I move on to the next chapter, I feel it's important to say that I am very glad AA is an option out there for people. It has saved countless lives, and for that I have gratitude. For some, labeling themselves actually helps them. I've heard a person say before, "I need that label to know I can never drink again." I think it's great for that person. However, we have to stop thinking there is such a narrow passage to success. There are a lot of options out there for people to get the help that is right for them.

CHAPTER 15

FINDING MY PEOPLE

For the first time in my life, I actually looked forward to my appointments with Dr. Allen. I thought it was because we were constantly seeing improvements, but it was so much more than that. It was a place where I could be authentically me. Everyone there knew what had happened and they celebrated my wins. Heck, the phlebotomist and I even became Facebook friends.

I remember a specific visit when Dr. Allen asked how I was doing and I told her that I felt like I was alone on an island. I felt alone not only in being alcohol free but also in my belief that I didn't have a disease that had doomed me to becoming addicted to alcohol. Was I just fooling myself? I had this looming fear about alcohol. I never wanted it to come back into my life. I finally felt good, and my days weren't filled with anxiety. But was I doing this wrong? <u>Society was telling me I was doing it wrong, and surely AA people thought I was destined to drink again because I wouldn't accept "who I was." To be honest, I was afraid.</u>

I could tell that my feeling lonely worried Dr. Allen. I'm sure she had seen so many people turn back to alcohol over things like this, and she knew that turning back would be fatal for me. I explained to her how I felt about going to AA meetings. They were helpful for other people, but they weren't helpful for me. Dr. Allen always respected my viewpoint on things; she actually listened. This was huge for me. She did encourage me to find a way to connect with people, so I listened to her and went searching.

Back to Google I went. Only this time it served me well. I typed in all kinds of questions and statements: "Why did my anxiety stop when I stopped drinking?" "I don't identify as being an alcoholic," etc. After I sifted through the paid ads for treatment centers, I found a podcast with a crazy name: *This Naked Mind* with Annie Grace. At an early age, Annie Grace was extremely successful in her career. She was traveling the world for business when she discovered that alcohol was no longer serving her. Now she is the bestselling author of *This Naked Mind* and *The Alcohol*

Experiment. I started listening to her podcasts and couldn't get enough. All the questions I'd been asking myself were explained, and things finally started making sense for me. Everything she talked about matched up with my journey. From the drinking aspect to the effects of not drinking, I was having constant "AHA!" moments as to why things felt and happened the way they did. I'll never forget the night Grady came home and I said to him, "I'm not afraid anymore." I had been so afraid of alcohol coming back and getting me one day because everything seemed so mysterious as to why I struggled in the first place and why I felt as good as I did once I was free from alcohol.

I joined one of Annie Grace and Scott Pinyard's challenges called "The Alcohol Experiment" so I could learn more. I was blown away by the group of over 2,000 people who were all in this online group to stop drinking. I listened to Grace and Pinyard coach people, and I knew that this was what I wanted to do as well. I finally wrote to Pinyard via a direct message on social media asking him whether they were ever going to train coaches in their method. Sure enough, in July of 2019, I found myself among my people. There were 60 of us in the room ready to be trained in the *This Naked Mind* methodology. We were from different places and had diverse journeys, but we all shared one common bond: we had found freedom from alcohol. Sitting in that room was a group of people from all over the world including health care providers, counselors, teachers, lawyers, yoga instructors, and stay-at-home moms. It was one of the most empowering feelings. I felt like Macaulay Culkin in the movie *Home Alone* when he ran outside screaming, "I'm not afraid anymore!" I wasn't afraid anymore. Not afraid to be my authentic self. Not afraid of the gossipers or naysayers. Most importantly, not afraid of that liquid in a bottle. <u>I had the knowledge and the science, and I had found my people.</u>

And yet there was still something lingering out there that I wasn't talking about—something that I just knew I could never share.

One day during the training, Annie Grace asked the group to think about a few things for homework that night. One of the questions was, "Where is your space not clear?" As soon as she said that, I knew exactly what my answer was. And even as I sat there ready to be trained as a coach, I thought to myself, *I will never open that door and talk about it. Ever.* So, lets talk about it!

CHAPTER 16

MY BATTLE WOUND

I just had an ultrasound done on my liver. It's something I have to do now every year or so. I flip-flop between ultrasounds and MRIs. It's never fun, and to this day, I cry every time I'm on that table. I'm grateful when the tech asks me to turn toward the wall. That way my tears can fall without being questioned whether the tech is hurting me. It has nothing to do with physical pain. The wound is so much deeper than that.

I frequently heard in the past and *still* hear about how resilient the liver is. "Oh, don't worry, the liver is the only organ that regenerates." Yes, our livers are amazing and resilient. But even the best fighter in the world will get injured if they get beat up too much.

As much work as I have done on myself, I still cringe when I see the registration papers pushed across the counter to me and see the diagnosis. "Alcoholic Related Cirrhosis." It makes me want to shrivel up and causes the ANTs to come flooding into my mind. Today, the person pushing those papers across the counter for me to sign was someone I knew. My heart sank. *Did she see the diagnosis? What did she think of me? Would she tell anyone?* The old me wanted desperately to come out and build protective walls all around me. It's the fear of gossip and judgment. Fortunately, my inner mentor kicked in and reminded me to take a deep breath and remember the words on that paper don't define me.

I've had to work around a lot of shame surrounding that diagnosis. For years I never spoke the words. Heck, I didn't even want to know how to spell it. I called it "the C word." **Cirrhosis.** I'd just pretend it wasn't there. I was still diligent about getting my screenings, though, so there would be a day or two every year when I'd have to face it. Whenever Dr. Allen calls me with the results from my latest scan, I know the C word is coming. She pauses when telling me, almost as though she knows what's coming next—a flood of emotion that I've stuffed down since my last appointment. Another good ol' ugly cry; you know, the kind where it's hard to catch your breath and talk. I get the news, am really sad for a day, and then I stuff it back down and move on.

So, that day at training when I was asked, "Where is your space not clear?" I knew I wasn't facing my cirrhosis diagnosis. Even then, as I was becoming a coach. Over time, it had become easier to talk about the other stuff, such as my severe anxiety and how I self-medicated with alcohol. But looking into the darkness behind the door of the C word … that was a whole other story. I remember thinking that day that there was no way in hell I'd ever talk about that. Period. I'm sure God had a loving chuckle over that one.

Because of my health journey, I knew that I wanted to talk to people in the medical community and share how I had come out of such a dark place. I knew I wanted to help people who were sick or got stuck like I did. And that meant having to eventually look behind that door. So I did what every coach should do and hired a coach for myself. Looking back, I see this was one of the best decisions I've ever made.

I met Lorna Wilson at a *This Naked Mind* live event and we hit it off. I immediately knew I liked her. We hadn't crossed paths at our coaches' training, but I knew she had been doing life coaching for years. As soon as we got into my history and health, she noticed the stuffing starting to show. My eyes would well up and my lip would tremble. I *might* have mumbled the word cirrhosis, but there's a good chance I was still using "the C word." Even with her, I was so stuck. So that's where we worked. One day, Lorna asked me to describe to her what cirrhosis was and explain it so she could understand it better. I said, "Well, it's like a small scab on my liver. You know, like when we fall down and hurt ourselves. I hurt my liver and it's my scab or scar. *It's my battle wound.*" When I said those last four words, it was like a weight was lifted. The lens through which I viewed my diagnosis had changed. Here I was carrying so much shame about something that was the aftermath of my body working so damn hard just to save me. I pushed and pushed, but it didn't give up. When it couldn't take it anymore, it had to stop. But it came back. I came back. And that was nothing to be ashamed of.

SECTION 3
LOOKING THROUGH A NEW LENS

CHAPTER 17

REMOVING THE INVISIBLE YOKE

We can't let the burdens we carry be our excuses to continue drinking. That's all they are—excuses. I wanted to blame my drinking on all the bad things that happened to me. And there was never a good time to stop; there was always an event coming up, a wedding, the holidays, or a stressful situation to get through. Don't be me. I thought that if I could just get through this one event … and then the next … then I'd ask for help and stop. I always had a reason to keep going.

When I look back on my journey, I see that the weight of the burdens I was carrying was just too much. First it was the weight of my anxiety. Then came the drinking. Then there was the true weight of my weakened body fighting to make a comeback. Even when it did come back, my diagnosis was like a yoke around my neck. It's amazing how heavy a label can be. If you aren't careful, you'll take on all the weight of the words that you believe to be true about a diagnosis. You can become the label. Your diagnosis can take over and suddenly it becomes who you are. It doesn't have to be that way.

When I opened that dark closet to face my diagnosis, I was overwhelmed with hopelessness. Why? Because of the picture I had painted in my head of what a person with cirrhosis looks like, what their life was like—just as I had done with people who were addicted to alcohol. I stepped into the world of Facebook support groups to see whether I could learn from people. Sadly, I found a lot of darkness there as well. It wasn't just hopelessness, it was helplessness, and I'm not sure which one is worse. But I know the combination is tragic. So many people are carrying around their diagnosis like a yoke around their neck. It's debilitating. It's also another motivator for me to speak out.

I'm tired of shame being my silencer. It doesn't have to be that way! You and I are not powerless. We are not helpless. We can do something about it and all of it is in our control. Cirrhosis is not a death sentence. I'm honestly healthier now than I was during all those years that I was trying to "fix it."

Once I learned about the connection between alcohol and anxiety, part of me was blown away. The other part of me was angry. Why was this the first time I was hearing about this? In all the years I had struggled with alcohol, nobody ever talked to me about what drinking alcohol does and how it makes everything worse.

So now I'm taking you on this journey with me. I'm sharing what I discovered through all my observing, my searching, and my living. I'm viewing life through a new lens—a lens that gives me a whole different perspective on this sneaky substance we call alcohol. It's a perspective that I think you'll want to hear and one I know can help you remove that yoke.

CHAPTER 18

REARVIEW MIRROR CHECK

While lying in a hospital bed, I couldn't believe what was happening to me. I had that clear picture in my head of the type of person things like this happen to, and it didn't look like me. But was I really so different? Are you? Let's look at the statistics and take a glimpse into the science of what's really happening regarding alcohol-related health issues.

THE STATISTICS

- The National Institute of Alcohol Abuse and Alcoholism shows that alcohol-related deaths more than doubled between 1999 and 2017.
- A 2018 study from the British Medical Journal saw a dramatic increase in cirrhosis-related deaths in the US from 1999 to 2016. In this timeframe ages 25–34 saw the highest increase. I was 36 years old when all of this happened to me. It gave me chills to know that I easily could have added to this statistic.
- Alcohol use is the third leading cause of preventable death in the US, and 95,000 people per year die from alcohol-related causes (National Institute of Alcohol Abuse and Alcoholism alcohol facts and statistics).
- A group of researchers assessed a group of 20 drugs and scored them on criteria related to overall harm. This study considered harm to both the user, and to the people who are around the user but not actually using the drug themselves. Alcohol scored as the most harmful drug, with an overall harm score of 72. Heroin came in second with a score of 55, and crack cocaine scored third with a score of 54.
- A study by Lancet 2018 reports there's no safe amount of alcohol and that no level of alcohol consumption improves your health. So no, that glass of red wine isn't good for your heart.

The bottom line is this: alcohol is killing people in droves. It doesn't discriminate by race or gender, and it clearly doesn't care how old you are. We have to stop romanticizing and prioritizing a substance that causes so much harm. If alcohol was released today as a new medicine and manufacturers were required to list all the side effects just like pharmaceutical companies do, that list might look something like this:

- Alcohol is the number one leading risk factor for premature death in ages 15–49.
- Use of alcohol during teenage years interferes with normal brain development and increases the risk for liver disease, heart disease, depression, stroke, and stomach bleeding.
- Alcohol increases the risk for cancers of the oral cavity, esophagus, larynx, pharynx, liver, colon, and rectum.
- Alcohol consumption is associated with an increased risk of female breast cancer. (So please stop putting pink ribbons on wine bottles and encouraging any type of drinking during breast cancer awareness month.)
- Alcohol increases the risk of drowning, violent falls, car crashes, and suicide.

If a brand new drink came out with all of the information that we now know about alcohol, people would think it absolutely insane to go out and grab a bottle.

THE SCIENCE

Our bodies and brains are truly amazing. Our bodies are always trying to maintain homeostasis, meaning keeping the body in balance. For example, when we get hot, we sweat. When our bodies recognize toxins in the blood, they get rid of them through urine. It's a constant

BLOOD ALCOHOL CONCENTRATION (BAC) AND YOUR BRAIN'S RESPONSE...

BAC RISING

It's that first dopamine hit —that temporary feeling of "ahhhh."

It lasts up to 30 minutes for the first drink.

The initial sips of alcohol signal your brain to release dopamine, the "happy" hormone, making you feel stimulated and energized.

However, the brain is also ordering the body to release adrenaline and cortisol, "stress" hormones, to counteract the depressant.

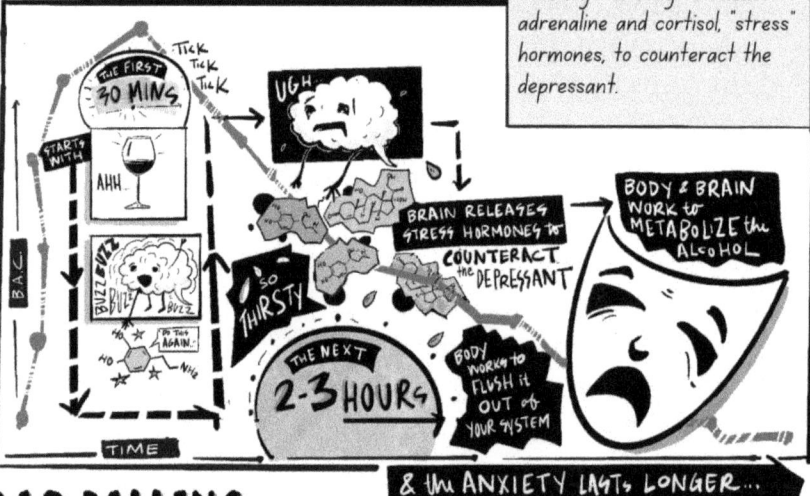

BAC FALLING

A 30-minute rise in BAC takes two to three hours to fall. While your BAC is falling, you feel irritable, thirsty, and eager to recover that initial "buzz."

The more you drink, the more the "happy" stimulant effects subside and are replaced by the depressant effects of the substance.

The first few sips at happy hour...

Later that night...

THE NEXT DAY

Many people WONDER WHY THEY FEEL SO ANXIOUS, especially after a night of drinking. It's that adrenaline and cortisol still flowing through your body.

job of balancing. I like to picture this as a ship that's out at sea, constantly moving with the waves sending it one way or another, ultimately just trying to stay upright.

Alcohol is unique in that it's both a depressant and a stimulant. When we first have a drink, our blood alcohol concentration (BAC) rises, which is what leads to that temporary feeling of euphoria. This is what hooks us. It's that dopamine hit—that feeling of "ahhhh" at the end of the day. But that feeling, that rise in our BAC, is very temporary. It only lasts around 30 minutes for a single drink. The brain, the captain of the ship, recognizes there's a toxin and a depressant on board, so it immediately orders the body to start the process of removing it. During this process, our bodies start releasing stimulating hormones such as adrenaline and cortisol to counteract the toxic depressant. Here's the kicker: that 30-minute rise in BAC takes about two to three hours to fall. Many people wonder why they feel so anxious the day after drinking. Well, it's that adrenaline and cortisol still flowing through your body.

I had no idea all of this was happening when I was drinking. This is also why studies show that even one drink disrupts sleep. That ship captain doesn't miss a beat. Anytime it recognizes the toxin, it counter-attacks. I find that so fascinating.

THE ILLUMINATION

When I stopped throwing my body off balance with drinking, my body was able to take a well-deserved break from having to dump stimulants into my system to maintain homeostasis. So there was a reason I felt that unusual sense of calm once I stopped drinking. There was also a reason I was throwing down all those popsicles. It's all about the science of the brain. When you drink alcohol, your brain gets a hit of dopamine. This dopamine response is a type of learning molecule that gives your brain feedback in response to a stimulus. So when you drink alcohol, the brain says, "Hey, that felt good, do that again." With each drink, your brain repeats this message. Over time, your brain learns that drinking feels good. So it's not shocking that alcohol is addictive. Sugar has the same effect, and it produces that same rush of dopamine in the brain. When I stopped drinking, my body was looking for that dopamine hit. At the time, popsicles did the trick. Oh, who am I kidding? Even before all this, I had a little issue with popsicles, Swedish Fish, and Starburst jellybeans. But I digress.

I gave myself a whole lot of grace during this time. At first, I was afraid I was simply trading in one addiction for another. But once my body realized that I wasn't going to be downing alcohol on a daily basis anymore, the sugar insanity calmed down. People have differing opinions on this topic, but in my case, those popsicles and jellybeans weren't making me say things I didn't remember, they weren't making it dangerous for me to drive, and quite frankly, they weren't going to kill me the way alcohol was.

Many other methods of combating sugar cravings when you stop drinking are also helpful. Here are some I found during my research:

- Get that heart rate up! Exercise can help so much. Don't overdo it. I couldn't do much at all during that time, but a walk outside was refreshing and helped a lot.
- Try to keep your blood sugar balanced. Some people do this by eating small meals throughout the day. Protein is your friend! Stay away from fads, and just stick with whole foods. I also learned that I'm not a nutritionist, so I recommend finding someone who knows more about this subject.
- Drink tons of water. This helps flush out toxins and will keep you hydrated.
- Eat real fruit instead of jelly beans. Honeycrisp apples are my favorite treat in the fall.
- Eat naturally fermented foods. Sauerkraut, kimchi, and kombucha are great options. Some people are afraid of the small

percentage of alcohol in kombucha. This is a personal decision, so you have to do what is right for you. Most kombucha has less than 0.5 percent alcohol. You'd have to drink nine bottles of kombucha to equal the average bottle of beer, which has 4.5 percent alcohol.

There are also so many things I learned after gaining experience with socializing. I want to share with you some things I wish I had known when I was at the beginning of my journey.

Not everyone deserves your story. I felt so much pressure trying to figure out what to say and what not to say. The bottom line is, most people haven't earned your truth yet. Hell, you may not ever know what your truth is, and that's okay too. When I first stopped drinking, I gave many people superficial stories including "I can't drink, I've had health issues" and "Wish I could, but I can't. I have all kinds of health issues going on. I can be your DD!" These stories were somewhat true, but they didn't reveal everything. There were some people I really cared about whom I wanted to share more with, but I was just trying to figure things out. As I learned more about what happened to me and why, I shared more with the people that mattered to me. Spend your energy figuring out how to deal with emotions. Create new healthy boundaries and develop new tools you can use when life throws you those zingers. Karen doesn't need to know the ins and outs of your journey.

Socializing can be difficult at the beginning, so set yourself up for success by having a plan for attending social events:

- Enlist the help of others. Ask a partner or friend to support you by letting them know that you're planning on not drinking during the event. Just putting it out there is so helpful.
- Make decisions ahead of time. What are you going to order to drink? If you're going to dinner, what are you going to eat? Check the menu out online before you go.

- Visualize the evening. Who are you going to see? What are some things you can talk about? What will the space look like?
- Prepare to ghost the host. Ghosting means you can leave at any time without an explanation to anyone, and it's always an option. The people pleaser in me used to spend so much time agonizing over when it was okay to leave and trying to figure out what to say to the host as to why I had to leave. It's time you started truly looking out for you. Besides, most of the time at a bigger event, people won't even know you left.

·•·•·•·•·•·•·•·•·•·•·•·•·•·•·•·•·•·

If you want to order a glass of wine or cocktail, by all means do it. If someone is uncomfortable with you drinking alcohol, they most likely wouldn't be out to dinner with you.

·•·•·•·•·•·•·•·•·•·•·•·•·•·•·•·•·•·

- Set your boundaries. A "maybe" means you will drink. Make a solid decision about what you want to do beforehand. At the beginning of my journey, I had a trip planned to see friends from high school. I agonized over what I was going to say about not drinking. It's not like we were huge partiers, but wine was definitely going to be involved. I even toyed with the idea of ordering a glass of wine at dinner but not drinking it. (By the way, though that's a common idea, it's a really bad one.) So in a group text,

I decided to let my friends know in advance that I wouldn't be drinking and that I couldn't because of my health issues. I love these ladies, and I know they care for me too. They'd hate to know that I struggled so much to tell them, but it was just part of the process for me. This was new to me, and I needed to figure it out. So letting people know in advance that you aren't drinking can be very helpful, especially in the beginning.
- Bring a non-alcoholic drink with you. This seems really simple, but it works really well when you're feeling uncomfortable about not drinking. My orange Yeti cup accompanied me to so many events, and still does. I'd fill it with my favorite sparkling water and bring it with me when socializing. I never got any pushback when asked what I wanted to drink, and I was able to simply say, "I already have something, but thank you!" I couldn't help but laugh to myself when people assumed that I had alcohol in the cup.
- Realize that people don't care. Yes, I had a few uncomfortable situations. But it's important to know that most of the time people don't care whether you drink or not.

And here's a side note for people who do drink alcohol:

(I can't help but picture Sophia from *The Golden Girls* when I say this. Those of you who love that show like I do will get where I am coming from here.) Picture it: You are out to dinner when the waiter comes up and asks what you want to drink. The person you're with orders a water with lemon. A flash of disappointment goes through your head, and you think to yourself, *Dang, are they going to judge me if I drink?* Your next thought is *Well, maybe they are just "one of those people who can't drink."*

One of two very common things happens next:

1) You ask them if it's okay if you order an adult beverage
2) You ask them why they aren't drinking

(Insert really loud "wrong answer" sound effect here.) Don't do these things. No matter how good your intentions are, just don't.

In the first scenario, the question makes things awkward for both you and your friend. If someone who isn't drinking is uncomfortable with you drinking, they wouldn't be out to dinner with you in the first place, or it's up to them to talk to you about their discomfort, preferably before the outing. I have experienced this so many times and have spoken to countless people who are trying to stop drinking and DREAD this question.

In the second scenario, the question needs to just stop being asked, period. We desperately need to normalize not drinking in our society.

Just order your drink. Nobody is judging you. Own it and move on.

CHAPTER 19

AND NOW A WORD FROM ... SMOKEY BEAR

It honestly pains me to hear about people taking that walk of shame to go pick up their "day one" chip after drinking again. When you drink again after you have successfully stopped for a while, it's crushing. If you could hear the internal lashing that one gives themselves after an experience like that, you would call it verbal abuse. *I'm worthless, I'm weak, I will never be able to beat this*, etc. goes on and on in their head like a broken record. According to traditional methods, they then have to walk up in front of the room and admit their defeat, and mentally go back to trying to get a day one again. So no matter how many days or years they didn't drink, all is lost and they are back to square one. "WHY?" I desperately want to yell out. "That's just not true! You just have a hot spot you need to put out!"

Smokey Bear is an icon used by the US Forest Service to educate the public about prevention of wildfires. In one of Smokey's campaigns, his message was loud and clear, "Only YOU can prevent wildfires." One of the things that the slogan meant to convey was that it was critical for people to completely extinguish campfires, because a single ember left burning, no matter how small, could spark a wildfire. I think there's a correlation here between smoldering embers and beliefs that we carry about how alcohol still serves us. To be successful on this journey, its crucial for the individual to address all those beliefs, burning embers, or the different hot spots and make sure they are out. Think about who is in the power seat here: YOU drank because you believed alcohol still served you in some way. No person or situation can make you drink, YOU just believe it will help you get through it.

So, when I refer to a hot spot, I'm referring to the belief that someone still has that alcohol serves them in some way. Some beliefs are conscious, so we are aware of them, which makes them easier to challenge and debunk. Our subconscious beliefs, on the other hand, can be tricky. We don't even know we have that belief until we are acting on it (and sometimes even our acting on it isn't enough to make us realize there's a subconscious belief pulling our strings). When you are on this journey, it's so important to sift through the layers of each subconscious belief. This is a glaring example of why people that announce they are going to stop drinking, or are forced by a loved one to stop drinking immediately, fail. They haven't addressed the reasons why they drink, or understood that their subconscious believes alcohol helps them in many ways.

You may go through this process and think you've totally debunked a particular belief and that you are cruising along in life just fine … Then an accelerant comes. When I refer to an accelerant, I'm referring to life's curveballs. It can be a divorce, loss of a job, the death of a loved one, etc. The accelerant doesn't have to be something negative; it can also be the promotion you've been working so hard for, an exciting new relationship, or other feelings of joy or celebration. We need to work on these beliefs: the belief that alcohol helps us through the hard times or rewards us in times of celebration. We need to extinguish all signs of life from that ember.

In my view, the only way to do that is to match up the science behind what alcohol does inside our body to our experience. For example, when I was able to step outside of my story that alcohol helped me with anxiety and look at the truth of what my life looked like (debilitating panic) and the science behind how alcohol affects the brain (the body responding to alcohol by releasing stress hormones that ultimately make you feel more anxious), I could start breaking down the belief and learning it's just not true.

Did alcohol really make that wedding more fun? Or did it just give you a headache the next day as you sifted through your foggy memories of what you did on the dance floor the night before?

How did alcohol help you with the loss of a person you loved or cared about? Did it numb you out for a while? Sure. But did you ultimately postpone any type of healing or dealing with the pain from it? Absolutely. Another thing I have seen several times is people going out after a funeral for someone that has died from alcohol, and meeting at their favorite bar to have a drink. This never fails to make my jaw drop. It's also a crystal clear picture of how people only blame the drinker and not the drink. You know what, no one would ever say after the funeral of someone who died of lung cancer, "Hey guys, let's all go out and have a smoke for Mary." It's insane. That liquid in the glass you're toasting with just killed your friend, and it was likely painful and slow.

In geology, hot spots can be a line of volcanoes deep within the earth.

A lot of people have hot spots around alcohol. These individuals don't see their drinking as problematic at all, and they believe that alcohol helps them with certain things such as, anxiety, stress, bonding with a partner, sleep, etc. The problem is, in life, we never know when an accelerant is going to come our way. A painful illustration of this was what happened during the pandemic in 2020. When they were taken out of their normal routine and were working from home (or not working at all) many people walking around without a "problem" with alcohol suddenly had a problem on their hands. I know many people that were shocked by how quickly they became daily drinkers. And the daily drinkers became shocked at how much more alcohol they could drink and still be "functional" the next day. People got a glimpse of the slippery slope that a ride with alcohol can become. Things got ugly. Sadly, instead of people recognizing that alcohol was becoming a real global problem, they shared humorous memes poking fun at how it was now acceptable to day drink. Don't even get me started on the Wine Mom memes. It makes me so angry to think about how the people in the alcohol/wine industry just sat back and enjoyed the show, while all the free advertisement just put dollars back into their already full pockets.

Meanwhile, behind the scenes, it was devastating. Not only were healthcare professionals bombarded with COVID-19 patients, but there was also a dramatic increase in alcohol-related illnesses during

AND NOW A WORD FROM ... SMOKEY BEAR

THE NOISE OF OUR
COGNITIVE DISSONANCE

CONSCIOUS THOUGHTS

I'll just put some RULES around my drinking.

I JUST NEED to HAVE BETTER CONTROL
ONLY on the WEEKEND
NO "HARD STUFF"
NO DRINKING at HOME
ONLY WINE
ONLY WHITE WINE
ONLY BETWEEN 5PM-9PM

In the noise of our cognitive dissonance, our BELIEFS will always prevail over our rules, data and intentions.

UNCONSCIOUS BELIEFS

BUT ALCOHOL HELPS ME HAVE FUN...
EVERYONE DRINKS
IT MAKES ME MORE CREATIVE
IT MAKES ME A HAPPIER MOM
I NEED IT TO REALLY UNWIND
I "DESERVE" IT
IT MAKES HARD THINGS EASY

Alcohol is KEEPING MY LIFE TOGETHER.

Our attempts to live by our rules fail until the beliefs about alcohol are addressed.

this time. One study showed hospital admissions for alcohol-related diseases such as cirrhosis and alcohol-associated hepatitis were up by 30 percent from the year before.⁵ Marriages fell apart and people lost their jobs because so many who used to be able to "hide" the fact that they were struggling couldn't hide it anymore. Liquor stores were deemed "essential" because there was fear that people would go into withdrawal from alcohol and suffer the consequences. It was a disturbing picture of alcohol and where it stands in our culture.

Some people that stopped drinking years ago still have hot spots that are unaddressed. They've been completely abstinent, but still believe alcohol serves them in some way. That subconscious belief is going to win out 99.9 percent of the time. Unfortunately, the pandemic shined a light on this issue as well. In March of 2020, there wasn't just a spike in demand for toilet paper and hand sanitizer. Alcohol was a hot commodity as well, with sales on a steep incline.⁶ Alcohol sales in the United States were the highest they had been in 18 years, with hard seltzers and read-to-drink beverages up 63 percent. There were many people who returned to drinking during the pandemic, after being alcohol-free for years. That dang hot spot wasn't put out. If someone believed that alcohol was still beneficial to them in certain ways, such as reducing stress, the pandemic sure put that belief to the test. Some people went back to what they *thought* served them.

Hot spots can also refer to wounds. However, when referring to hot spots regarding alcohol, these wounds aren't on the surface being irritated all of the time. These wounds go deep and are unaddressed traumas. When we drink, we are numbing wounds. Pushing them

---

⁵ Cahan, Eli. "As Alcohol Abuse Rises amid Pandemic, Hospitals See a Wave of Deadly Liver Disease." *Los Angeles Times*, Los Angeles Times, 8 Feb 2021, https://www.latimes.com/california/story/2021-02-08/alcohol-abuse-pandemic-hospitals-liver-disease.

⁶ Castaldelli-Maia, Joao M., et. al. "The Concerning Increasing Trend of Alcohol Beverage Sales in the U.S. during the COVID-19 Pandemic." *Alcohol* vol 96 Nov 2021, pp 37–42., https://doi.org/10.1016/j.alcohol.2021.06.004. Accessed 21 Jan 2022.

deep into our subconscious. When we remove the numbing agent, these wounds surface and seem to come out of nowhere. Trauma looks different in every individual. I am no expert, but I will share what one trauma looked like in me.

I was a new mom, and had been alcohol-free for about a year at the time. I was totally in my element. I had dreamed of becoming a mama since I was a child. Grady was a doting Dad, loving his new role in life. Our daughter was only a few months old when this horrible feeling started rising up in me whenever he would start snuggling with her or just look at her adoringly. It was this fierce feeling of needing to protect her. I could feel it burning in my chest. One time, it was just so strong, I yelled out, "Stop looking at her like that!" Poor Grady. I knew what I was feeling was completely uncalled for, but I just couldn't control it.

Thankfully, I knew someone who specializes in trauma, and I shared with her what was going on. She said "Oh yeah, that's a trauma revisiting you." Well it sure was waving its hands and letting me know it was still there, alive and well. I went through therapy called EMDR, Eye Movement Desensitization and Reprocessing, and it worked wonders. I was so grateful. I'm sure Grady was too.

Those deep hot spots or wounds are something I bring up to whoever I work with now. If you were drinking heavily at the time of getting therapy for a trauma, there's a good chance that you still need some work around it. This isn't something that you should attempt to heal on your own in a meeting or a Facebook group. It's important to find someone who is trained in trauma to get the help you need and deserve.

Leaning into the reasons someone starts drinking too much, or starts drinking again, provides powerful information. It's a guide for showing you where that ember is still smoldering and needs to be extinguished. Unfortunately, the stigma of admitting a struggle with alcohol is still hanging around, and the fear of being labeled a "problem drinker" or an "alcoholic" is the ultimate mute

ADDRESS THOSE BELIEFS

There's a correlation between those SMOLDERING EMBERS, and the BELIEFS we carry that alcohol still serves us...

In both the case of a person using alcohol to cope with stress, anxiety, poor sleep or unpleasant emotions

AND

a person who quit drinking but who still believes that alcohol helps with stress, ect.,

A single ember left burning, no matter how small...

YOU MUST EXTINGUISH THOSE BELIEFS

...can spark a WILDFIRE.

EXTREME STRESS will exacerbate or reignite the habit if either one believes that alcohol offers the best relief.

Under EXTREME STRESS the person that used to be able to control their drinking is now self-medicating with a substance that is addictive. They may be unable to stop.

AND

The person that quit drinking but still believes that alcohol is what helps with stress turns back to alcohol as a way of SURVIVAL.

button. People keep it inside and go back to the mindset of, "I'll just take care of this on my own" because they are scared of what others will think.

I dream of a day when people can talk about alcohol the same way they do sugar. At that Bible Study in Georgetown, someone once shared their struggle with sugar. They went into detail about how sometimes they would wake up in the middle of the night, go to the kitchen, and eat several slices of pie or whatever cookies they had on hand. The women who filled the room nodded with empathy as she told the story, sympathizing with her. This is a perfect example of viewing things through different lenses. What if that same girl was telling her story, but instead of it being pie or cookies she ingested, it was several glasses of wine? I promise you the response wouldn't have been the same. I'm not saying those women wouldn't have felt compassion; they would have, because they were amazing women. But I promise you there would've also been some judgement, even if it was buried deep. That "A for alcoholic" label would've crossed people's minds. Schooled by Dr. Phil shows, some people might've put that girl in a particular category they thought they knew everything about.

People addressing their relationship with alcohol are up against not only their own beliefs, but our society's beliefs as well. It's hard, but addressing our own personal beliefs is the best thing we can do to keep moving forward. Once that hot spot is extinguished, you create a new pathway to follow when life throws you curveballs. Recently, I went through a horrible bout of anxiety mixed with feelings of depression. I used all the tools in my toolbox and was at a loss at what to do. I was absolutely miserable, and so was everyone around me. I started thinking about when I used to live every day feeling that anxious ... My heart broke for the old me; I have no idea how I did it for so long. The powerful thing about this experience was it showed me that my hot spot, my belief that alcohol was the only thing that helped, was not only extinguished, I was repelled at the thought of it. My body knew wholeheartedly that drinking alcohol was the last thing I needed to do.

Processing those internal flames that need to be snuffed out doesn't mean you're flawed. It just means that you have one more piece of the puzzle that, when finished, will lead you to freedom.

CHAPTER 20

CHANGING THE NARRATIVE

When it comes to alcohol, we must change the script. You'll commonly hear in AA meetings that the definition of insanity is doing the same thing over and over and expecting different results. Well, that's exactly how I feel about how our society approaches the issue of alcohol. It is glorified by the public, and readily sold at more locations than not. I recently went to our favorite ice cream shop and the woman behind the counter said "I know how much you love our Italian Ice, well, get ready to love it even more." Unfortunately, I knew what was probably going to come next, and I was right. She said with excitement, "We will now have 'spiked' ice cream and icees!" YET, if you struggle with the addictive substance, you are an alcoholic, you are different, you are an addict, you are flawed. The whipped cream on top of that spiked ice cream is that there is only one way to get help for your genetically flawed body. That's absolutely insane. The climbing rate of alcohol-related deaths should make it clear enough that the narrow thought process here isn't working.

You won't find me standing in the picket line wanting to ban or demonize alcohol, but man I'm sure going to fight like hell to start speaking the truth about it. Our children deserve better. People often ask me what I'll tell my daughter about alcohol. The answer is … the truth. The truth is, she can make her own choice one day whether she wants to drink or not. I just want her to know what she's putting in her body.

The story that "some people can drink and some can't" has set us up to fail. The demand that "you stop drinking or else" has set people up to fail. The well known thought of "you have to hit rock bottom" in order to change your relationship with alcohol is a very dangerous lie. My personal journey took me about as low as you can go, but I've met countless people that have decided they didn't like how it made them feel anymore. The story and the language that so many people have been told about alcohol needs to change.

This change requires an honest conversation about health. We should be able to freely discuss our concerns about drinking without fear of judgment or a label. However when the topic of alcohol is brought up, many times defensive walls go up, or assumptions are made. My Dad has always been a big believer in writing letters. You can get down all the things that you really want to say without interruption. Also, the person can do what they want with it, including reading it again, maybe hearing it a little differently the next time they pick it up. I've never been much of a letter writer, but here I am writing a book. There's so much I want to say, and I know this book is just the beginning. There's so much I want to say to healthcare providers, and there's a lot I need to say to that person that was looking in the mirror years ago.. Feeling scared and hopeless. So I guess I will try a letter.

DEAR HEALTHCARE PROVIDER

You truly have a big job. I cannot imagine the load you have on your back. People have so many expectations of you, and there is so little time.

Alcohol use disorder is wreaking havoc on your patients, and there is a very good chance alcohol has impacted you or someone you care about in your personal life. The problem continues to grow, and we need to do something about it.

You are in a powerful position to make a difference in someone's life. I want to ask you to challenge your own beliefs about alcohol. What story have you been told? Does alcohol play a certain role in your own life?

Imagine the patient who is struggling with alcohol. What do they look like? Is it just the GOMER who comes in for yet another scalp laceration, or is it also the soccer mom who needs a glass of wine in the evenings to deal with her kids, or the lawyer whose blood pressure has been hard to control but you've never really inquired about how many cocktails he has each night? Do you get frustrated with them, and feel like they are doomed, or do you realize that they have a treatable condition that you can help them admit, face head on, and then overcome? There is a lot of power in the word "hope," and you have the ability to give someone that power. Does that ever make you sit back and think, "Wow"? It should. Giving patients hope is powerful and can change the direction of someone's path.

I have come across many physicians who treated me as "less than" because of my alcohol history. One encounter was particularly humiliating; the guy was not nice at all. After some time, though, I was able to ask myself whether I could really blame him. How many years had he been seeing people slowly kill themselves with alcohol? How many warnings had he given them that they needed to stop? He knew that if they just stopped drinking, things would be different. They would live. But they seldom heeded his advice. How maddening would that be?

I once watched a physician speaking to a large group of people at an Alcoholics Anonymous conference. He made a few derogatory jokes about "us alcoholics" as is commonly heard at meetings like that. Then he went into how treating patients like "us" is difficult. The basis of his conversation centered on telling patients that certain things are bad for them—using shrimp as an analogy. He explained that when you tell a patient that shrimp is bad for them, or that they are allergic to shrimp, they stop eating shrimp. But not "those alcoholics." When you tell them to stop drinking alcohol, they just can't seem to do it. That was his comparison of "normal people" and alcoholics. Are you kidding me? The fact that he compared the two blew me away. When was the last time you saw a shrimp commercial? Or have you ever had your coworkers ask if you wanted to go out for shrimp? What about when you were younger and going to a party? Did you sit around with your friends and wonder whether shrimp was going to be at the party, or did you bring shrimp to the party to feel cool? You get my point. Trying to compare the two makes no sense.

This substance has seeped into almost every part of your patients' lives and they are scared. How can they tell you how much they are drinking when they are hiding that fact from themselves? When I was in the hospital, I was asked multiple times per day how many drinks I was having each day. Staff members clearly had this box they needed to check off. Since it was a teaching hospital, residents would frequently come into my room to ask the question. I was lying there looking like a pregnant Oompa Loompa with ascites and high bilirubin. Did getting that number from me really matter at that point?

I've talked to so many people who want so badly to talk to their physicians about their fear of drinking too much, but they are just too scared to make that move. Shame can be the ultimate silencer and a huge block that stops us from saying something and moving forward.

Alcohol makes your job so much harder. It sends you searching down so many rabbit holes when the whole time it has been the culprit of a patient's health issues such as anxiety, high blood pressure, insomnia … The list is long.

I cannot imagine the difference it would make if we could just change the conversation. Make this a safe subject to talk about. I think it would be transformative.

Thank you for listening,
Karla

CONCLUSION

DEAR 2014 ME

I know you'd go through it again in a heartbeat—the horrible pain, the swollen belly, the inability to stand on your own, the fear, the gossip, the uncertainty—to be where you are today, right now.

This dark valley you're walking through will turn out to be one of the most beautiful gifts life has given you. I know you don't see it, but I want you to know the possibility of what life can be like. It does require something from you, though: You gotta show up. You have to make the decision that you don't want this for your life anymore. Your loved ones can't make that decision for you. You're in the driver's seat.

Has alcohol hijacked your brain? Absolutely it has. But I want you to listen to your soul. Stop blaming the world around you and start looking in the mirror. Everything you need to get started is right there.

When you were in the hospital, you prayed for God to give you another chance. You begged for your life not to be over. Never in your wildest dreams would you have thought that you'd not only get the chance to live but also be ever so grateful for the experiences you've had.

Be grateful for what you've gone through because it gave you a perspective you can share with others in the hope that they don't have to stand where you stood. Maybe they can catch themselves halfway down and realize it's time to climb back up.

Those who are on the valley floor like you were need your unique perspective of what exactly alcohol does to them. Your perspective can be not only a gift but also a unique superpower that you give them. You saw the darkest side of what alcohol does, the truth behind all of the sneaky filters it carries. You climbed out of the valley knowing full well what it looks like up close and personal.

That flame that lives inside you now is your motivation to move forward and tell your story. Each person who shares their struggle with you, each commercial you see trying to teach your daughter how romantic alcohol is, is like a bellow that gives that fire of yours the oxygen it needs to keep sharing, keep writing, and keep living fully.

You came tumbling down, over and over. It left you with bumps and bruises and a few scars, but it didn't break you. It doesn't have to break you, the reader, either.

I believe in you, and you believe in me. Our story is far from over. So let's go live it.

AFTERWORD

Faith. That's what I think of when I reflect on Karla's journey. The dictionary defines faith as complete trust or confidence in someone or something. It takes faith to walk a hard road, to change your life, to push forward when you have hit a dead end again and again, and with an uncertain end. I remember the first day I met Karla and I knew she had something that was amiss with her liver, but I never would have guessed the root cause. She was kind, funny, functional, and welcoming to a young physician in a new town.

It was when I asked her in my office what was wrong that I discovered her fear and the root cause of her medical condition. I remember how surprised and grateful I was that she was willing to confront her alcohol use head on. That is what sets her apart—her ability to take on difficult situations and learn and grow. Throughout that first year, there was a lot of fear—on my part and hers. Here was a patient I had come to care about personally and professionally. I was fiercely protective of her confidentiality and privacy. When she was initially admitted with alcoholic hepatitis, I feared she may not improve without liver transplantation and discussed that with her and her husband. But, despite all of the odds, she did continue to improve and stabilize. When she returned home, we saw each other every other week initially, then once per month. She steadily made one change after another. She began to exercise, to improve her strength and endurance. She changed her diet to include healthy foods. And this helped. But I want to be clear, her journey was not without speed bumps. She struggled with neuropathy and polymyalgia rheumatica. She worked religiously with a counselor to overcome daily anxiety.

It's rare to find a patient who is resourceful, persistent, and relentless in their pursuit of health. After caring for patients for many years who lack the ability or insight to understand that choices have consequences, Karla was a breath of fresh air. To watch her emerge from alcohol use into a new mindset that let her become happier, take responsibility for her health, and gain control of her anxiety has been one of the great joys of my career. When she called to tell me she was going to become a mother, I knew her life was on a path to change for the better. There simply are no words, and although the work has undoubtedly been hers, her faith has carried her through. Faith that things will get better, faith that there is a different path. Her path has taught me many things that continue to influence how I teach residents, other physicians, and even friends to think about addiction and treatments. Recovery is not one size fits all. It is imperative to listen to those who struggle with addiction and respond with kindness, patience, and support. I do believe in tough love and some of my favorite physician mentors favor this approach. But, for me, support as a healthcare provider has the ability to change someone's life.

It is with great admiration and awe that I recognize Karla's unique ability to help others identify a path to recovery that is different from what is typically accepted. Despite the fact that AA was not a good fit, she has gone to meetings to receive her chips as a reminder of how far she has come (these have been some of my favorite pictures to receive). We have viewed it as a celebration of the work she has put in. When she discovered *This Naked Mind* and the alcohol experiment, everything began to click and she felt as though she was making progress for the first time; without shame, without fear … only faith. Faith that this time will be different.

Karla has been given a second chance and she intends to use that to help others. She intends to educate medical professionals on what addiction looks like now and what recovery CAN look like now. She intends to use that second chance to help others walk the hard road toward change. To empower others to be relentless in their pursuit of a better life, and to have an unshakeable faith that no matter how many times they have fallen short, this time can be different.

Sarah Allen, M.D.

REFLECTION

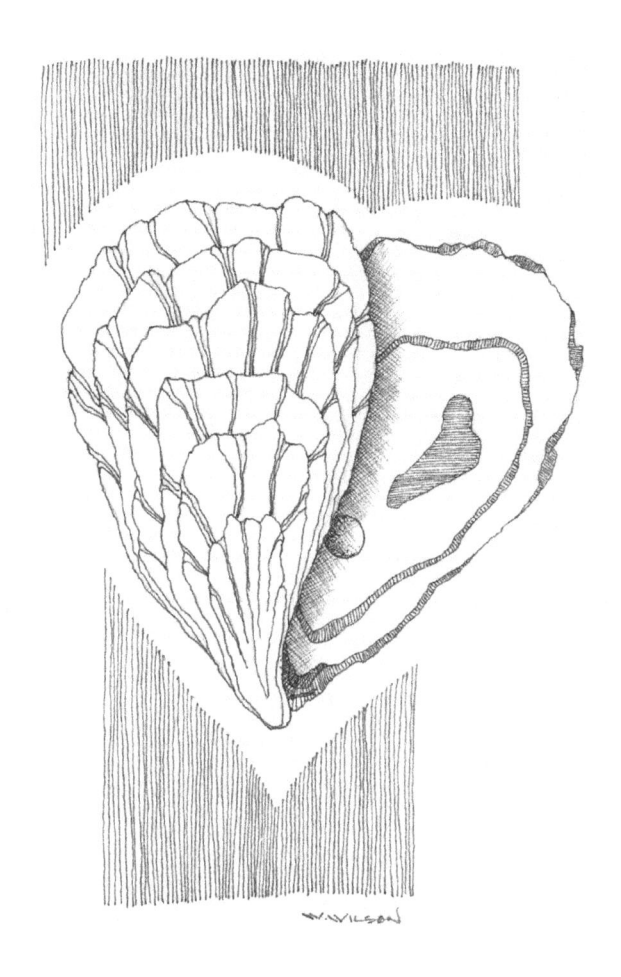

This book is dedicated to those that aren't here
to share their story anymore. I see you.
I will keep sharing my story so people
may understand yours a little more.

To the reader:
The world is your oyster. It starts with you.
You can do anything you set your mind to.
Yes things may get hard.
Choose your hard.

There is so much beauty on the other side.

When you finish this book,
Pass it along to someone you believe
Would benefit from hearing Karla's story

You can find Karla Adkins at:
www.karlaadkins.com
Facebook – @karlakadkins
Instagram – @karlakadkins

ABOUT THE AUTHOR

Karla is on a mission to normalize not drinking and to help people make the shift from feeling shame to being courageous. After a life-altering event, her perspective on life changed, and through that experience, she created a safe, judgment-free zone where people can talk about their alcohol fears without being labeled.

Drawing from her own experience as well as her certificate as a Certified Senior Coach through This Naked Mind, Karla helps put people back in control of their lives by empowering them with the tools and knowledge they need to remove their desire to drink.

In her free time, Karla spends time with her family including her husband, daughter, and dog on the East Coast of South Carolina.

CPSIA information can be obtained
at www.ICGtesting.com
Printed in the USA
BVHW020947160922
647225BV00019B/417